Health and Wellbeing
SPHE 3

Anne Potts

Nodlaig O'Grady

The Educational Company of Ireland

Edco

First published 2018
The Educational Company of Ireland
Ballymount Road
Walkinstown
Dublin 12
www.edco.ie

A member of the Smurfit Kappa Group plc

The paper used in this book comes from Managed Forests in Northern Europe. For every tree felled, at least one new tree is planted

ISBN: 978-1-84536-778-7

Book design: Design Image
Cover design: Graftrónaic
Layout: Graftrónaic
Editor: Barrett Editing
Editorial Assistant: Michael Kemp
Proofreader: Jane Rogers

Photographs and illustrations: *iStock.com*: (Strand 1: Yayayoyo, OJO Images,Chris Ryan, gbh007, fotostorm, asiseeit, dolgachov, asiseeit, sissy_12, Ranta Images, monkeybusiness images; Strand 2: IPGGutenbergUKLtd, Zhukow, Misspixels, Dean Mitchell, FabrikaCr, SchulteProductions, portokalis, ermingut, msderrick, 3dalia, Smithstock, wbritten, willierossin, FatCamera; Strand 3: Alashi, goodynewshoes, kali9, jacoblund, goodynewshoes, Mixmike, eli_asenova, jeremyiswild, fstop123, monkeybusinessimages, monkeybusinessimages, adekvat, JackF, Connel_Design, mandygodbehear, Ranta Images, MmeEmil, prudkov, Daisy-Daisy, igor_kell, wundervisuals, M-I-S-H-A; Strand 4: Skynesher, pixelfit, oleksagrzegorz, monkeybusinessimages, AnaBGD, Eva-Katalin, monkeybusinessimages, lilly3, Daisy-Daisy, bowdenimages, omgimages, fstop123, alpertti, RichLegg, Flamingo_Photography, FatCamera, track5, franckreporter, binabina); *Shutterstock.com*: (Strand 1: Rawpixel.com, CuteCute, fizkes, Lorelyn Medina, daniaphoto, Artisticco, dashadima, GaudiLab, Catalin Petolea, Aleutie, Africa Studio, Rawpixel.com, ZDragon, ZDragon, inLite studio, designer491, Monkey Business Images, Tiko Aramyan, Gustavo Frazao, Rawpixel.com, HitToon, Monkey Business Images, Roi and Roi, g-stockstudio, Rawpixel.com, 3D_creation, yayayoyo, ZDragon, ZDragon, Rawpixel.com, Denis Cristo, Tashatuvango, Pretty Vectors, aastock, Babiina, Heijo, Hriana, Rawpixel.com, Rawpixel.com, Lopolo, Lara Cold, 3D_creation, ImageFlow, Cultura Motion, John David Bigl III, Iryna Inshyna, SpeedKingz, Wiktoria Matynia; Strand 2: pixelheadphoto digitalskillet, iMarzi, Iakov Filimonov, Everett Historical, Svetography, wavebreakmedia, Monkey Business Images, ibreakstock, David Orcea, Firma V, Daisy Daisy, michaeljung, Photographee.eu, goodluz, S_L, Sudowoodo, Click and Photo, Syda Productions, Arleevector, Phoenixns, VectorsMarket, koya979, Monkey Business Images, Iakov Filimonov, Nyamol Ds, Vector Tradition SM, Teguh Mujiono, Denis Cristo, Zoriana Zaitseva, Iryna Inshyna, tommaso79, Syda Productions, northallertonman, SpeedKingz, Caftor; Strand 3: Oneinchpunch, byskop, Dean Drobot, G Allen Penton, Ljupco Smokovski, sianc, Creativa Images, Oleg Golovnev, Claudia Paulussen, Iakov Filimonov, Monkey Business Images, LightField Studios, Bonezboyz, Kheng Guan Toh, wenchiawang, northallertonman, hartphotography, SpeedKingz, Lorelyn Medina, Maria Symchych, Cultura Motion, Rawpixel.com, iordani, polya_olya, Cultura Motion, Rawpixel.com, Dejan Dundjerski, igor kisselev, Denmorgancom, Natalia Sheinkin, Lorelyn Medina, Hermin, yaistantine, Mjak, Maria Starus, poosan, Oguz Aral, pio3, Lolostock, LoopAll, Rawpixel.com, MJTH, VLADGRIN, Answer Production, Yuliya Yesina, NAS CREATIVES, Timmary, mikecphoto, whitemomo; Strand 4: Sabphoto, Africa Studio, kenary820, Rawpixel.com, RelisaGranovskaya, Sarah Holmlund, CREATISTA, Debby Wong, Featureflash Photo Agency, BAKOUNINE, JStone, Tinseltown, Leonard Zhukovsky, Featureflash Photo Agency, Natalia Deriabina, art_of_sun, TrifonenkoIvan, Good_Stock, Jaguar PS, Cookie Studio, Kevin McKeever, Asfia, dondesigns, BestPhotoPlus, Leremy, WaiveFamisoCZ, Barry Barnes, marekuliasz, LeventeGyori, Dean Drobot, Syda Productions, Antonio Guillem, MaryValery, Bunny Rose Photography, Africa Studio, Monkey Business Images); *Alamy Stock Photo/Alamy.com*: (Strand 2: Dan White; Strand 3: Paul Fearn; Strand 4: Allstar Picture Library, Glenn Harvey, Granger Historical Picture Archive); *Gettyimages.com*: (Strand 1: Kyodo News; Strand 4: Ramsey Cardy. Phillip Massey, David Maher, Matthew King, AGF, BANARAS KHAN, CELLOU BINANI); Simon Smith (Beehive Illustration); Igloo Animations; Irish Water Safety.

Disclaimer: Web references in this textbook are intended as a guide for students and teachers. At the time of going to press, all web addresses were active and contained information relevant to the topics in this textbook. However, The Educational Company of Ireland and the authors do not accept responsibility for the views or information contained on these websites. Content and addresses may change beyond our control and students should be supervised when investigating websites.

Contents

Introduction

Welcome to *Health and Wellbeing: SPHE 3*. We hope you enjoyed everything you learned and the skills you developed through following this programme over the past two years and are now ready to start on year three. This three-year programme is designed to help you to become (or remain!) a confident, happy, healthy and connected young person.

The aims of the health and wellbeing Social Personal and Health Education (SPHE) classes are to give you the space to:

- Learn about yourself
- Care for yourself and others
- Make informed decisions about your health and wellbeing.

Health and Wellbeing: SPHE 3 is designed to involve you in your own learning, by using theory and activities which make you think about the topics, discuss the issues and apply what you have learned to your own life. You will also find follow-up references listed: websites, videos and help agencies. This textbook is full of interesting information and activities which make learning stimulating, such as drama, collage, quizzes, animations, debates, film-making, newspaper articles, cartoons, and PowerPoint and oral presentations.

To ensure that you get the most out of SPHE, at the beginning of each unit you will find the **Learning Outcomes** for that unit, which you can tick off as you achieve them. There is also a list of **Key Words** which are explained in clear, simple terms throughout the text, **Did You Know?** boxes with interesting facts, and research findings and background information on each topic.

To help you to keep track of your learning there are **Learning Logs**, **Assessment – Check your learning** activities and **Unit Reviews**. Work you have completed can be stored in an SPHE folder or electronically in an e-folder. Your oral literacy is developed using debates, class presentations and small group and class discussions, while your digital literacy is helped by producing videos, making slide presentations and taking online quizzes and tests. The use of charts, graphs, surveys, percentages and ratios helps to improve your numeracy skills.

Finally, *Health and Wellbeing: SPHE 3* includes an extra section providing guidelines to assist you in organising a themed week on the topic of wellbeing.

We hope that you continue to enjoy and benefit from your time in post-primary school and that *Health and Wellbeing: SPHE 3* helps you to achieve this!

Anne & Nodlaig

Digital Resources

The *Health and Wellbeing: SPHE 3* digital resources will enhance classroom learning by encouraging student participation and engagement. To aid lesson planning, PowerPoints and animations are **referenced in the textbook** using the following icons:

PowerPoints – cover a range of key topics, including planning for effective study and exams; healthy and unhealthy relationships; and sex, sexuality and sexual health.

Animations – pose scenarios for students to discuss in class.

Visit **www.edcolearning.ie** to access the *Health and Wellbeing: SPHE 3* e-book and digital resources, which also include **worksheets** to accompany the animations and **weblinks** for each unit. **Exclusive additional resources and information** are available at **ie.reachout.com/edco**, in partnership with **Reachout.com**.

UNIT 1 Self-Management 1 – Setting Goals and Targets

Learning Outcomes:

This unit helps you to:

1. Think about where you are at the start of third year and where you'd like to be at the end of the year ◯

2. Draw up some class ground rules to guide your work in SPHE ◯

3. Set goals and SMART targets for your third year in post-primary school. ◯

(Tick off as you complete them.)

KEY WORDS

Goals
Goal-setting
Learning environment

Welcome Back!

Hopefully after your summer holidays you are feeling energised and optimistic about the year ahead. You are a year older and able to take more responsibility for yourself, your work in school, and your own health and wellbeing.

This year you have the challenge of preparing for examinations and tasks associated with your Junior Cycle Profile of Achievement. In this unit, you will learn how to take responsibility for your work, how to meet deadlines and how to reach targets.

A good start is essential to success. The first thing you need to do is to set goals. Having goals to work towards will encourage you to keep going, even when times are tough and you don't feel like studying any more.

KEY WORDS

Goal

Something you are trying to do or achieve.

Goal-setting

Making a plan to achieve your goal.

success

Goal-setting for third year

Think about where you are in relation to the year ahead. Are you prepared and ready to go, or do you need a little help? Maybe you are not sure where to start. In first year you explored the importance of having balance in your life – remember Pat (see *Health and Wellbeing*: SPHE 1, page 27). Look at Activity 1, which will help you to think about your life in general, not just in relation to your school work.

Activity 1

Where am I now?

Think about two areas in your life:
- Your social life and your friends
- Your academic life and your school work.

Look at the picture of the tree and circle the figure(s) that best represent(s) where you are now. Maybe you feel healthy and self-confident on one level, but on another level feel that you need a lot of help with preparing for the Junior Cycle Profile of Achievement.

1. Why did you select this figure or figures?
_____
_____
_____
_____
_____

2. Would you like to be somewhere else on the tree? If so, where would you like to be?
_____
_____
_____
_____

3. Would you like to be in different places for different aspects of your life? If so, why?
_____
_____
_____
_____
_____

4 What steps can you take to reach where you want to be at the end of this year?

_____

_____

5 Who, and what, could help you?

_____

_____

Activity 2

Ground rules

In your SPHE classes in first and second year you will have drawn up some ground rules to help you work together in a safe and respectful way. In groups of four, come up with as many rules as you can remember and write them in the space below.

_____

_____

_____

As a class discuss all your rules and come to an agreement on the five most important rules. For each rule, say why it is important and how it will help your work in SPHE.

Class ground rule	Reason
1 _____	_____
2 _____	_____
3 _____	_____
4 _____	_____
5 _____	_____

Activity 3

Thinking ahead

You will need a copy of your second-year school report for this activity.

> Setting targets helps you to approach your work in an organised and structured way.

1 Look at the results on your report and think how you would feel if they were your exam and assessment results at the end of the Junior Cycle. Would you feel happy, sad, angry, disappointed or regretful?

2 Think about the subjects you did well in on your second-year report and what helped you. What might have prevented you doing well in other subjects?

3 In the grid below write down the subjects that you are studying this year. Include all your subjects. Then list the results you got in your second-year summer exams and assessments.

4 Jump forward to Christmas, or your mock exams, and write down the results that you would be happy to get.

5 Now look forward to next September and write down the results that you would love to see on your Junior Cycle Profile of Achievement. You should set these results as your targets for next year.

Subjects	Summer 2nd year results	Results I would like to have at Christmas or in my mock exams	Results I would love to see on my Junior Cycle Profile of Achievement

Did You Know?

The greatest sprinter of all time, Usain Bolt, who is the holder of world records in the 100 metres (m), 200 m and 4 x 100 m and an eleven-time world champion, believes in setting goals.

He said:
'It is important to set goals in life. I set mine to the highest standard I can achieve.'

Setting Targets – Think SMART!

Setting targets helps you to achieve your goals. Following the guidelines below will help you learn how to set SMART targets and goals.

Specific: A specific goal would be, 'By the end of this week I will understand and know the periodic table'. A vague goal would be, 'Know a bit more chemistry.'

Measurable: Measure you progress towards reaching your goal. Use past and sample exam questions and your ongoing results, e.g. 'I will answer all questions on the periodic table from the past four years' exam papers', or 'I will improve my result in science from Achieved to Higher Merit by Christmas.'

Time-frame: Set a time-frame for your goal. Identify how much time you need and when you can do it, e.g. 'I must spend 15 minutes each evening revising poetry, so that by the end of the month I have learned everything I need to know about six poems.'

Relevant: Set goals that will help you to achieve something that is important to you now, e.g. if you want to study biology or chemistry at Leaving Cert, it would be important to work towards improving your grades in science in the year ahead.

Attainable: Set a goal that you can achieve. Your goal should match your ability and interests. If you are struggling with a subject that you find boring or hard it is unrealistic to expect to get a 'Distinction' on the higher-level paper.

S pecific
M easurable
A ttainable
R elevant
T ime-frame

Activity

4

SMART Goals

Look at your second-year report again. Choose one subject in which you want to improve. Using the guidelines above, set SMART goals!

Specific:

_____

_____

Measurable:

_____

_____

Attainable:

_____

_____

_____

Relevant:

_____

_____

_____

Time-frame:

_____

_____

A good learning environment

How well you do in school is greatly influenced by your learning environment, both at home and at school. In school, it is important that everyone contributes to ensuring that your class is a safe and respectful place where everyone can learn and achieve to the best of their ability. If your school or class is a good learning environment it will make it easier for you to achieve your targets and goals. Let's explore this further.

KEY WORDS

Learning environment

The place where teaching and learning take place, including the physical space, e.g. your classroom or where you study at home, as well as the people in it with you; other students, your teacher and so on.

Activity

5 Work contract

Brainstorm the different things that would make your SPHE class a good learning environment. Write five of the ideas in the speech bubbles below and, as a class, identify the six most important points. Then write them into the work contract on page 7, beginning each statement with 'I'.

SPHE Work Contract

1 _____

2 _____

3 _____

4 _____

5 _____

6 _____

Signature: _____

Date: _____

Knowing what makes a good learning environment is one thing. Being committed to maintaining that environment is another! How committed are you to playing your part?

Sign the contract to show your commitment to playing your part.

LEARNING LOG

Identify two things you can do to ensure success in the year ahead.

1 The most important thing I need to do now is

2 I also need to

3 I can contribute to making our class a safe learning environment by

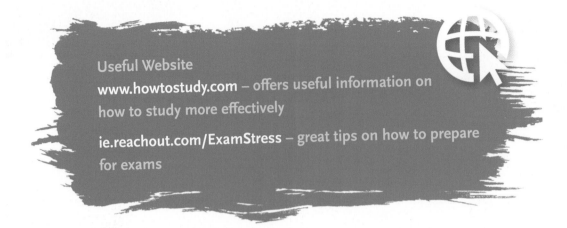

Useful Website

www.howtostudy.com – offers useful information on how to study more effectively

ie.reachout.com/ExamStress – great tips on how to prepare for exams

Review of Unit 1: *Self-Management 1 –*
Setting Goals and Targets

1 In this unit I learned about _____

_____

_____

2 I think that this will help me _____

_____

_____

3 I liked _____

_____

_____

4 I did not like _____

_____

_____

5 I would like to learn more about _____

_____

_____

6 This topic links with (another topic in SPHE or another subject) _____

_____

_____

UNIT **1** Self-Management 2 – Making the Most of Your Study Time

KEY WORDS

Time management
Balance in your life
Plan
Planning
Exam techniques

Learning Outcomes:

This unit helps you to:

1. Mange your time efficiently
2. Prepare for assessments and examinations, especially your Junior Cycle Profile of Achievement
3. Develop strategies and techniques for success in completing assignments and preparing for exams to help you to succeed in your final year of the Junior Cycle.

(Tick off as you complete them.)

KEY WORDS

Time management

Organising your time so that the right amount of time is allocated to each activity that you need to do.

Organising Your Time

In the previous section you discussed how to set personal goals for the coming year. If you have already set some goals, well done! To help you to achieve these goals the next step is to learn about time management and how to study for exams. You also need to develop strategies and techniques to help you to succeed in your school exams.

Some people are good at organising their time and they fit lots of activities into their day. Other people have a long 'to do' list and spend more time thinking (and talking!) about what they have to do than achieving anything. They often end up doing very little.

Managing your time is a very important skill. When you are properly organised:

- You will feel more in control
- You will be less stressed
- You will enjoy life more.

Activity 1

Timewatch

To find out how to manage your time better, first you need to look at how you are spending your time now. On the clock, mark the total amount of time that you spend on different activities each day, e.g. travelling or hanging out with your friends. If there are other things that you do, e.g. babysitting or visiting your grandparents, mark these in too and label them. While no two days are the same, try to work out an average time for each day.

Activity	Time
Sleeping	_____
Travelling	_____
Eating	_____
Watching TV	_____
Internet	_____
Messaging	_____
Relaxing	_____
School	_____
Study/homework	_____
Hobbies/sport	_____
Exercising	_____
_____	_____
_____	_____
_____	_____

Remember

As a growing young person, you need between 9 and 9½ hours' sleep each night.

To stay healthy, you need to do a minimum of 60 minutes of physical activity a day, five days a week. Did you build this in?

Compare your time clock with those of your classmates. On a scale of 1 (very pleased) to 5 (unhappy), indicate how pleased you are with how you spend your time. Then answer the questions.

1 What are the things you spend most time doing?

_____

_____

2 What are you most unhappy about spending time on in your 24-hour day?

_____

_____

3 What would you like to have more time for?

_____

_____

4 Decide what is stopping you from changing how you organise your time and write two things you can do to improve your time management:

(a) _____

_____

(b) _____

_____

You could try doing Activity 1 for a Saturday or Sunday to see how you spend your time at the weekend. It might help you to plan your time more effectively.

Balance in Your Life

As you learned in *Health and Wellbeing: SPHE 1*, it is important to have balance in your life. It is as unhealthy to spend all your time studying as it is to spend all your time on your phone messaging your friends, watching TV or playing computer games.

How do you achieve balance in your life?

Categorise your priorities

Work out what is essential for you to spend time on and what is not essential. It is necessary to spend time on sleep, exercise and eating healthily. What else is important in your day?

Spot what needs to be changed

In Activity 1, you learned what changes you need to make in order to organise your time better. Identify what makes it difficult to change, and start by doing something about this. Think about the questions below to get you started.

KEY WORDS
Balance in your life
Making time for all the different elements that make up a healthy life – including **work** (school, homework and study, helping with jobs at home), **rest** (sleep and relaxation) and **play** (sports, music, reading, meeting friends and so on).

1. Do you find it hard to say 'no' to people?
2. Do you end up doing things that you don't really want to do?
3. Are you a perfectionist and unable to leave something until it is perfect, no matter how long it takes?
4. Are your friends' goals different from your goals? If so, plan a set time that you will spend with your friends and pursue your goals away from them.

Plan your time

Make a plan. Keep it in front of you and, better still, share it with your friends and parents/guardians. This will help you to stick to it.

KEY WORDS
Plan
A set of decisions about how you will do something.

Tips for success

- Be realistic in setting your goals and your targets. If you are overly ambitious, you will get fed up and scrap the whole thing. Allow for interruptions. Celebrate and reward yourself if you finish something early.

- Use a yearly calendar to keep track of important dates such as Christmas tests, mock exams, deadlines for assignments and practical work. Put in times when you might have other activities, like a heavy sports schedule or music exams. You will have to plan your study around these events.

- Make a weekly list of what you want to achieve. Do this at the start of each week.

- Have a daily 'to do' list of smaller actions that are possible to achieve in a day. Enjoy crossing them off your list throughout the day.

- Figure out when you work best and do your hardest tasks at these times. Save easier, 'brainless' tasks, such as sorting out books and sports gear for the next day and making your lunch, for when you are tired. Don't leave this until the morning!

- Have a long-term goal and believe in it. Use it to motivate you when you get fed up.

- Keep a visual record of what you have to do and your progress. Focus on what you have done so far – never on the amount you have left to do!

- Think in 10-minute timeframes. People often delay doing things until they have a long stretch of time and end up not starting at all. In 10 minutes you can learn a piece of French vocabulary, do one maths problem, write a 'thank you' note or wash up after dinner.

- Don't wait for the right time – do what you can now!

- **Always leave your mobile phone in another room.** You won't be tempted to look at it if it is out of sight! Even short messages break your concentration and replying uses up your time.

Activity

2 Planning

KEY WORDS

Planning
The process of deciding in detail how you will do something before you do it.

Long-term planning
Using your school journal as a guide, make a plan for this year from now up until your exams next June. If they are not already included, put in the dates for school exams, the mock exams and other important dates and deadlines, e.g. for class-based assessments. Add in any other significant dates such as family holidays, sports and other events.

Medium-term planning

Take from now until your mid-term and make a detailed plan of the areas of your life that you want to improve. Plan what you want to achieve in this time. This might include doing more extracurricular activities, schoolwork or the progress you want to make in your personal life, like organising a Halloween party. Be as detailed as you can in planning what you want and how you are going to achieve it. Do this on a page and place it on a wall where you can see it each day.

Short-term planning

Make out a simple 'To Do' list for the next 24 hours. This should be made up of TATs: Tiny Achievable Targets. For example:

- Do my homework
- Buy something for Aidan's birthday
- Revise coastal erosion

- Finish Irish essay
- Write up science experiment
- Find a costume for the school play.

The one thing that I would like to change about how I plan is
_____
_____

The first step I am going to take to help me to manage my time better is
_____
_____

LEARNING LOG

Planning for Effective Study
Revising for your exams

PowerPoint

In *Health and Wellbeing: SPHE 2*, you looked at study skills that you could use to help you to remember what you learn in school. Now you are going to explore the **skills and techniques that will help you to study for exams**. We will focus on the best ways to revise the work that you have covered so far for the exams part of your Junior Cycle Profile of Achievement.

To start, you need to build on the skills you learned last year– summarising, mind maps, mnemonics and flash cards – as you need to find ways to revise and remember three years' work for the Junior Cert exams. To do this you are going to use a technique known as SQ4R.

SQ4R stands for Survey, Question, Read, Recall, Revise and Review.
This technique is explained on the next page.

SQ4R

1 Survey

Survey (read) the material to be learned, noting the headings, diagrams, and especially the introduction and conclusion. This gives you an overall picture of the piece.

2 Question

Write down questions that you want the text to answer. This makes learning more meaningful and will help you in your exams. Questions on a topic such as coastal erosion might be 'What are the different types, causes, signs, prevention and consequences?' Use past and sample exam papers to guide you in selecting questions.

3 Read

Read the entire piece using the techniques you learned in *Health and Wellbeing: SPHE 2*: highlighting, mnemonics, flash cards or mind maps. Try to find the answers to the questions you asked yourself in stage 2. You may have to read the piece more than once.

School Report Card

Subject	Grade
English	Distinction
Science	Higher Merit
Maths	Higher Merit
Irish	Merit
Business	Pass
Technical Graphics	Higher Merit
CSPE	Distinction
History	Distinction
Geography	Higher Merit

6 Review

(Go back over it) Before you finish a study session, review everything. This will help you to draw together what you have learned and should give you a great feeling of accomplishment.

5 Revise

Open your textbook and compare what you have written with the facts of the piece. Note the areas that you didn't know well, or at all, and revise these. Don't waste time revising the parts that you know.

4 Recall

Close your textbook and see how much you remember. Using points, write the answers to the questions you chose. Don't look at the notes you made. Don't be tempted just to answer in your head. If you can't write the answer down in words, points or diagrams, you don't know it!

Knowing HOW to study boosts your self-confidence and results in improved motivation and better results.

Activity 3

Practising SQ4R

As a class, take a piece of text in a subject that everyone is studying, such as history, geography or science. Select a page that you have already studied and revise it using the SQ4R technique that you have just learned.

1 How much of the material could you recall?

_____

2 What helped you most to remember?

_____

3 What could you improve?

_____

4 What changes do you need to make to help you to revise more efficiently? Remember what you learned about **study skills** in second year.

_____

Tips for revising

-  **Find a study buddy:** Some students find it helps them to revise if they work with another person. Older students frequently work in study groups. A 'study buddy' should be someone similar to you in ability and motivation. Otherwise, you might find you are slowing one another down or distracting each other.

- **Plan**: Work out what you hope to revise each day and keep going until it is done. Then reward yourself with a treat, such as having something nice to eat, listening to music or going for a jog.

- **Check up on what you don't understand:** If you find material that you don't understand while you are revising, make a note of it and ask your teacher about it the next day or the next time you have that subject.

- **Use past or sample exam papers:** They will be a good guide to your study. Try to answer the questions in the way that you will be expected to answer them in the exam.

Before you complete the Learning Log it might be helpful to review the Three Ss of effective study – Stuff, Space and Schedule (see *Health and Wellbeing: SPHE 1*, page 22).

A good place for me to study is _____ because _____

Someone I could revise with is _____ because _____

What I find hardest about revision is _____ because _____

Something I can do to help improve my study skills is _____

LEARNING LOG

Coping with Exams

No matter how much some students have revised in preparation for their exams, they often don't do as well as they would have hoped, or possibly as well as they could have done, because they don't know how best to approach the exam paper. Many students are not sure exactly what is expected of them in answering the individual questions.

Let's look at how you can manage how you approach exams and learn ways to improve your performance.

KEY WORDS

Exam techniques
How you apply what you know in answering questions under exam conditions.

4

How well do you handle exams?

Do you study hard but fall apart on the day? Do you spend ages on one or two questions and rush to get the others finished? Alternatively, do you think you did well, only to find that you completely misread the paper? Do this quick quiz and find out your exam style.

	Statement	a/b/c
1	I start answering questions before I have read all the instructions.	(a) Always (b) Sometimes (c) Never
2	In multiple-choice questions, when I come to the answer I think is the correct one I stop reading the other choices.	(a) Always (b) Sometimes (c) Never
3	When I get my exam paper I scan it for questions I recognise, then I quickly scribble down the main points of these topics before I forget them.	(a) Always (b) Sometimes (c) Never
4	I make sure I know how many marks each question is worth.	(a) Always (b) Sometimes (c) Never
5	If I finish the exam early, I hand it in and start studying for the next one.	(a) Always (b) Sometimes (c) Never
6	I start with the questions that I find easiest.	(a) Always (b) Sometimes (c) Never
7	I answer all the questions on the paper, even if I am not asked to.	(a) Always (b) Sometimes (c) Never
8	Before I start the exam, I have worked out how much time I am going to give to each question. When my time is up I leave it and start the next question.	(a) Always (b) Sometimes (c) Never
9	I make a brief outline of answers to essay-type questions before I start to write them.	(a) Always (b) Sometimes (c) Never
10	After the exam, I talk about it with my friends.	(a) Always (b) Sometimes (c) Never

Scoring: Your teacher will tell you how to score your answers in the grid below:

Q	a/b/c	Score
1		
2		
3		
4		
5		
6		

Q	a/b/c	Score
7		
8		
9		
10		
	Total	

Interpreting your score

0–30 = You have some problem areas and you are definitely not getting the most from your exams. Have a look at the next section to see where you are going wrong.

35–65 = You are doing some things well, but there is room for improvement if you are to maximise your marks. See if you can identify some areas for improvement.

70–95 = Congratulations! You have a planned, calm approach to exams and with a little help could be doing the very best you can possibly do.

Two things I do well in handling exams are:

1

2

Two areas I need to improve on are:

1

2

LEARNING LOG

Remember

Before you begin your exam take a 'Mindful Moment' and do your 'Sixty-second breathing meditation' (see *Health and Wellbeing: SPHE 1*, page 175).

Check out the 'Five-minute stress busters' in Strand 4, Unit 1 (see pages 141–143) to help you keep calm as you study for your exam.

Activity 5

Help me out!

Write two points as answers to each of the questions in the speech bubbles.

From what you learned in Activity 5 and have heard from the others in your class, make an exam advice card with the best advice on preparing for and doing exams. Include what you think are the six most important pieces of advice. Keep this advice where you can see it!

Activity 6

Exam advice

Activity 7

The language of exams

Marks are often lost when you don't understand what you are asked to do in your exams. Below are some words commonly used in exams. Match them up with their meanings.

Stress how things, events, problems or qualities are different from each other.

Show the similarities and resemblances between events, people, places and so on. If it is appropriate, mention the differences too.

Define

Summarise

Compare

Contrast

Explain

Outline

Diagram

Write exactly what something means, in clear, concise terms.

Give reasons for events or differences and try to suggest or identify causes. You may have to show evidence from the text.

A drawing, chart or graph. These should be labelled and there could be a written explanation required as well.

Give the essential elements, showing the main points and leaving out the minor details.

Give the main points in shortened form.

Write down (a) two things you are doing well as you prepare for your exams and (b) two areas you need to improve on.

(a)

(b)

Assessment – Check your learning

Design a slide presentation of no more than **eight** slides describing how best to prepare for your Profile of Achievement exams and assessments next June. Make out your own eight slides and then see what ideas other people in your class have come up with. As a class, decide on the eight most important tips for a final presentation. Your final slide could be an interesting motivational quote.

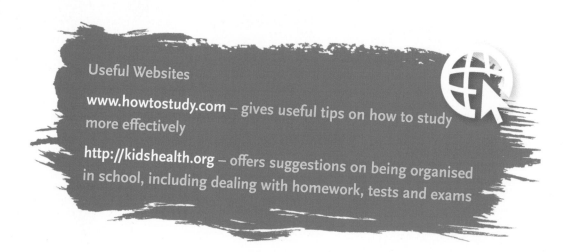

Useful Websites

www.howtostudy.com – gives useful tips on how to study more effectively

http://kidshealth.org – offers suggestions on being organised in school, including dealing with homework, tests and exams

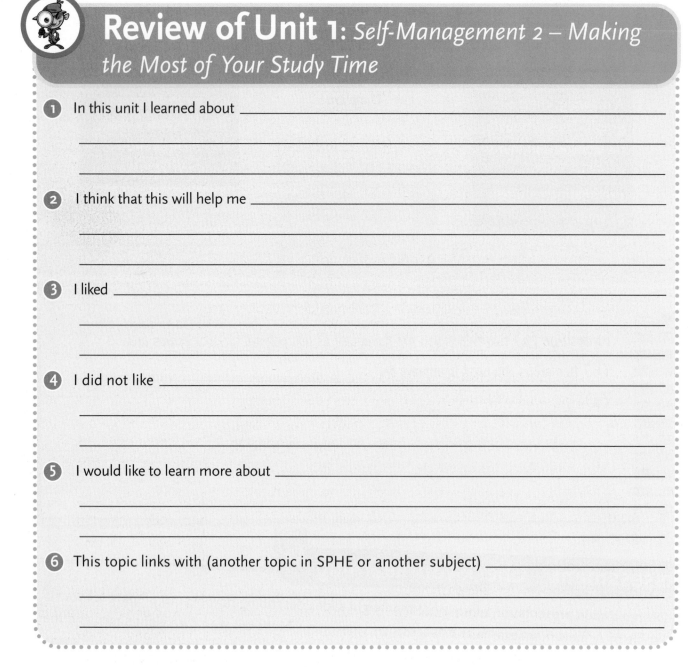

Review of Unit 1: *Self-Management 2 – Making the Most of Your Study Time*

1. In this unit I learned about _____

_____

_____

2. I think that this will help me _____

_____

_____

3. I liked _____

_____

_____

4. I did not like _____

_____

_____

5. I would like to learn more about _____

_____

_____

6. This topic links with (another topic in SPHE or another subject) _____

_____

_____

Who Am I?

UNIT 1 Self-Management 3 – Your Wellbeing

Seeking Help, Advice and Support

In years one and two of your SPHE course you explored many aspects of your general health and wellbeing. You learned that understanding what good physical health means will help you to make wise decisions about what you eat, what physical activity you should do and what rest, relaxation and sleep your body needs, so that you can have a healthy lifestyle. You also know that being healthy is about more than looking after your physical health – you need to take care of your mental health as well. Having the skills to look after your mental health means that you can get along with people in your life, have good confidence and self-esteem, and are able to manage and express your feelings in an appropriate way.

You discussed when you need to ask for help and where to get such help. For example, if you are stressed about schoolwork, or have had a row with your friend or have felt sad for a long period of time. Up to now you may have talked to family and friends but sometimes you may feel more comfortable seeking help from other people. It's important to look at other sources of information about your health and wellbeing. You'll learn more about how to do this in the activity on page 24.

KEY WORDS

Reliable resource
Blog
Vox Pop

KEY WORDS

Reliable resource
A resource you can depend on.

HELP
GUIDANCE
SUPPORT

Activity 1

Where would you go?

You can find information and advice about your health and wellbeing in many places. For a few minutes think about the range of issues related to health and wellbeing that a young person of your age may need help with. When you need to get help or information where could you go?

With your class brainstorm the different sources of help that you know about. They might be people, places, agencies, media sources and the Internet. Write as many as you can think of below.

Where would you go?

Did You Know?

Online health searches have become the third most popular activity on the Internet.

In pairs, identify the most popular sources of help and answer the questions on it below.

1 Who might use this source?
_____

2 What makes it attractive to young people?
_____

3 What, do you think, are young people looking for when they go here for help or information?
_____

4 Give three reasons why.
_____
_____

5 Is this a reliable source of help? How do you know?
_____

6 Why might a young person use this source rather than talk to a trusted adult or help agency?
_____

7 Would you be happy to refer a friend to this source of help or not? Why/Why not?
_____

Activity 2

Dr Internet

PowerPoint

As your teacher reads out each of the statements below about the Internet, hold up your red, green or orange traffic light page at the back of your book to show what you think – choose green if you agree, red if you disagree or orange if you are unsure. Mark in your answers below. Then rate yourself depending on how safely you think you use the Internet to find information about your own health and wellbeing. Your teacher will clarify any misinformation you may have.

Statement		Agree	Disagree	Unsure
		Green	Red	Orange
1	The Internet is the best source of information and advice.			
2	It is better to 'surf the net' before asking a trusted adult or going to a doctor.			
3	Information or advice online is always from a reliable source.			
4	It is important to be able to tell the difference between facts and opinions in relation to advice and information.			
5	Information on the Internet is always up to date.			
6	It is always better to check out who is providing the information or advice before taking it.			
7	Personal blogs are a better source of help than more professional sites.			
8	It is essential to know how to check a website for its reliability and accuracy.			
9	Most young people go to the Internet as a first port of call.			
10	If I am unsure about information or advice I find on the Internet I should check it out with a trusted adult or professional.			

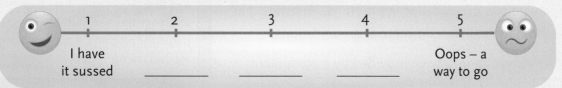

1   2   3   4   5

I have it sussed _____ _____ _____ Oops – a way to go

Even if a website is, or says it is, a medical resource you should still take the same safety measures as you would on any other site or on social media. Revise the 'Safe Surfing' tips that you have already explored in your SPHE classes (see Health and Wellbeing: SPHE 1, page 36).

25

Can you trust it or should you trash it?

Remember

Staying safe online

Not all websites about health are reliable sources of advice or information. Read through the 'Questions to ask' and the 'Answer tips' for each one below to ensure that you'll be a savvy surfer. Then complete the Learning Log.

Evaluating the web source

- **Relevance:** Does the website have what I'm looking for?
- **Purpose:** To inform?
- **Accuracy:** Is it fact or opinion? References?
- **Author:** A medical expert? Is the author biased?
- **Currency:** How up to date is the medical info?

Questions to ask about websites

1 Is the website trustworthy? How can you tell?

Look for the **'About us'** page and check out who operates the site. Websites that end with .net, .gov, .edu, and .org are usually more trustworthy because they are set up by government, not-for-profit organisations or academic institutions. Websites that are .com are usually commercial organisations.

2 Is the information/advice provided by a competent person, doctor or health professional?

Anyone can put information on the Internet, through blogs, YouTube channels, setting up their own website and so on. They may not be an expert or even have accurate knowledge. Be wary of following this advice.

3 Is the information accurate? Does it meet my needs?

The accuracy of the information depends on what questions you have asked and the expertise of whoever answered. Being as accurate as you can in your description ensures a more exact response. Know the difference between 'Fact' and 'Opinion'. (Find this out, if you don't know!)

KEY WORDS

Blog

An informal website or web page which is regularly updated, usually set up by one person or a small group, and has a conversational style. Blog means 'weblog' and bloggers usually share their thoughts on things they like or dislike, or on particular passions, e.g. fashion, music, football teams, recipes and so on.

4   Can I understand the information?

   If you don't understand it, ask for clarification. Don't act on what you don't understand.

5   Might the website be biased in any way?

   Be aware! Is the website trying to advertise, promote or sell you some product or service? If so, it may be biased. If you think it is biased try to find a website with the opposing viewpoint.

6   Has the website been updated recently?

   Responsible websites will be updated regularly.

7   Does the website ask you to give your email details or ask personal questions?

   Before you disclose personal information online make sure you know who you are dealing with and how the information will be used. If you are unsure, check out the site's privacy notice or ring them and ask. Don't give out your personal details. Review the section on cyber safety in *Health and Wellbeing: SPHE 2*, pages 45–49.

8   What is the website's privacy policy?

   Check this out. You don't want your personal information shared with others or sold on to another organisation.

9   Would you be happy to tell your doctor, parents or other trusted adult that you had sought and/or taken on board the information or advice from this website?

   If you don't feel comfortable doing this maybe you need to think twice about using the Internet as your only source of information and advice on anything to do with your health and wellbeing.

LEARNING LOG

Describe what you think are the four most important features of a website that you might use to access information or advice about any aspect of your health and wellbeing. Say what the risks of not considering these points might be.

Activity 3

Practice makes perfect – www.barnardos.ie

Throughout your SPHE programme you have been provided with websites which are safe, reliable and provide information and advice to teenagers on all aspects of health and wellbeing. Log on to www.barnardos.ie and search the website for information or advice for one of the issues below and then answer the questions. Have a class discussion about your findings.

Someone is saying mean and hurtful things about me on Twitter. It's awful. As well as that I've started getting anonymous text messages making fun of me. I'm scared and wish it would stop. I haven't a clue what to do but feel like I want to crawl into a hole. Help.

I'm fifteen and in third year, trying to study for my exams. My dad has a problem with drinking and this is causing trouble at home. I don't know what to do. I can't talk to anyone as I don't want anyone else to know what's going on but I have to do something.

My friend has changed a lot recently. She never comes out with us and she says she just feels sad all the time. I think she might be depressed and I'd like to help her but I don't know what to do.

I'm fifteen and I was wondering how much sleep do I need? I find it hard to get to sleep and I am tired every morning. I can't concentrate in school and I'm falling behind. Can you help?

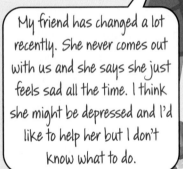

Checklist

1. Give three indicators that www.barnardos.ie is a safe and reliable website:

   (a) _____

   (b) _____

   (c) _____

2. Was the website easy to use? Why/Why not?

   (a) _____

   (b) _____

   (c) _____

3 How recently has the website been updated?

_____

4 Is there anything to suggest that the information or advice is biased in any way? If so, what?

_____

5 Would you be happy to recommend this website to a friend? Why/Why not?

_____

6 What made this website attractive/unattractive to you?

_____

7 What, if anything, might put you off using this website or make it difficult to use?

_____

Assessment – Check your learning

Carry out a Vox Pop among students in your class to find out what services are available in their area that supports the wellbeing of young people. Include the findings in your school newsletter.

KEY WORDS

Vox Pop

Comes from the Latin words _vox populi,_ shortened to vox pop, meaning 'voice of the people' or popular opinion.

Becoming Independent

Learning how to stay safe is an integral part of becoming more independent. When you become independent you start finding your own identity and taking more responsibility for yourself. This may not always be plain sailing. In _Health and Wellbeing: SPHE 1_ and _Health and Wellbeing: SPHE 2_ you explored a range of situations in which your personal safety might be put at risk, and how to stay safe at home, on the roads, around water, on a farm and when you are online. Let's explore other kinds of personal safety.

Safety while babysitting or at home alone

Now that you are older, you may find yourself in situations where you are given greater responsibility and you are in charge of your own safety or the safety of others. In these situations, it is important to know what to do if anything goes wrong. Look at the activity on pages 30–31 to identify ways of staying safe while you are home alone or babysitting.

Activity 4

Difficult dilemmas

Working in groups of three, read the three situations below and use the 'Dilemma board' to decide what you would do if you found yourself in *one* of them. Your teacher will tell you which dilemma to work on. On the board write:

- Your dilemma
- Four or five options (things you could do)
- A reason for each option
- Your final decision.

(Alternatively, you could copy the template onto a large page and keep it in your SPHE folder.)

Dilemma board

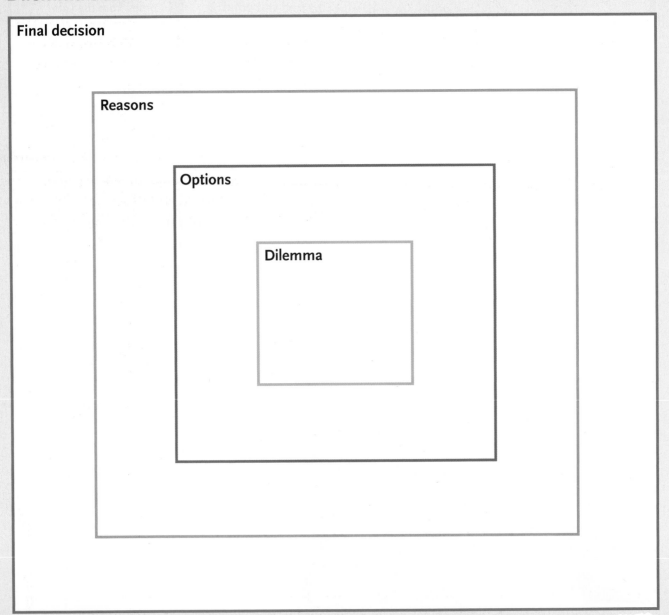

Situation 1: Home alone

You are at home on your own. It is winter and dark outside. You settle down to watch TV and the doorbell rings. You have been told not to answer the door. It is late and you are not expecting anyone to call. You try to ignore the ringing but it continues. You are getting really worried.

What do you do?

Situation 2: Babysitting

You are minding your neighbour's children, aged six and two. The two-year-old is asleep and you are just getting the older child to bed when your friends arrive at the door. They have brought a box set for you all to watch together. You were not expecting them and you are not sure if your neighbour would be happy if you let them in.

What do you do?

Situation 3: Getting home safely

You regularly look after the baby of friends of your parents. They live about 10 kilometres from your house and usually the baby's dad drives you home when they get in. But this evening you can tell that he has been drinking. He still wants to drive you home.

What do you do?

PowerPoint

Using what you have learned in this section, write five useful tips for someone who is taking up a babysitting job for the first time this summer.

1

2

3

4

5

LEARNING LOG

Useful Websites

www.kidshealth.org – in the 'Teen' section there is lots of useful information on all aspects of babysitting

www.mindme.ie – offers hints and tips to teenagers on all aspects of babysitting and associated responsibilities, how to prepare yourself, what you should know and do, and how to handle emergencies

www.suzylamplugh.org – an organisation that aims to reduce the risk of violence and aggression through campaigning, education and support

Review of Unit 1: *Self-Management 3 – Your Wellbeing*

1 In this unit I learned about _____

_____

_____

2 I think that this will help me _____

_____

_____

3 I liked _____

_____

_____

4 I did not like _____

_____

_____

5 I would like to learn more about _____

_____

_____

6 This topic links with (another topic in SPHE or another subject) _____

_____

_____

UNIT 2 How I See Myself and Others

Learning Outcomes:

This unit helps you to:

① Explore ways of enhancing your self-esteem and that of others ○

② Appreciate your uniqueness and that of others ○

③ Learn the differences between the private and public you. ○

(Tick off as you complete them.)

Being able to appreciate your own uniqueness is the first step in learning how to appreciate and value the uniqueness of others. In first and second year you explored the importance of nurturing your self-esteem and that of others. This is an important building block in developing healthy relationships and friendships. For

KEY WORDS

Uniqueness

Being special and different from other people in many different ways – how you look, your personality and your talents and gifts.

Nurture

To care for, look after and help improve or grow.

Self-esteem

How much you value yourself – how you think and feel about yourself.

example, in new relationships or friendships you should be open and honest with others but without putting yourself at risk. Don't tell somebody too much about yourself until you get to know them better.

Let's look at how you can improve your self-esteem, so that your friendships and relationships can become more meaningful and fulfilling. Some of the many ways you can do this are explored in the next activity.

Activity 1

Being unique – nurturing your self-esteem

How you feel about yourself has a great influence on the way you behave towards others and on the way you treat yourself. Read each statement and then give one example of how you think it will help you to enhance your self-esteem and how it might affect the way you behave towards yourself and towards others.

Statement	
Be open and honest with others without putting yourself at risk	Know your values and live by them
Have respect for yourself and others	Don't compare yourself with other people
Learn what is right for you and follow through on it	Think positively about what you do and say
Do things that you are good at and enjoy doing	Take responsibility for yourself and your decisions
Recognise your strengths	Avoid people who put you down

Masks – what you see and what you don't see

Throughout history people wore masks for all sorts of reasons – sometimes for fun or for disguise and also for protection. As you go through life you get to know yourself more through your friendships, relationships and how you cope with day-to-day living. Sometimes it's not so easy and you pretend to be somebody that you are not so you will feel more included and accepted. Most people don't want to be judged or rejected so, for example, you might hide your true feelings out of fear of upsetting others or fear that other people might see the real you. This is like wearing a mask to hide the person you really are. Being able to share what's behind the mask helps.

As you get to know someone better, you develop a relationship and share more of yourself. You find things that you have in common, and a sense of trust develops. You share things in a way that lets your relationship grow. You often discover things about yourself that neither you nor the other person knew before.

Communicating and sharing things about yourself also enhances your self-esteem and the self-esteem of the other person. Revealing your true self, the person behind your everyday mask, allows your friendships and relationships to grow.

Activity

2

Behind the mask

Look at these masks.

The Public Me

The Private Me

1. On the front of the 'Public Me' mask write your name and add in some things that other people know about you and that you are happy for others to see, e.g. good at sport, studious, likes to speak in public and so on. This represents the 'public you'. You can use symbols or drawings as well as words.

2. On the second 'Private Me' mask write your name and add some things about yourself that other people don't know, things about yourself that you hide from the world, e.g. feel really self-conscious in PE or are scared of being alone in the house and so on. These represent the 'private you'. **You can draw symbols or pictures rather than writing words, if you prefer.**

3. In groups of three, discuss as much as you wish of what you have written or drawn and what it means to you. If you are happy to do so, say why you want to hide what's on the private mask from other people. Talk about how you have changed since first year and how, and why, you may protect your privacy now in a way that you didn't when you were younger.

Then complete the Learning Log.

LEARNING LOG

1 I found Activity 2 easy/difficult because

2 Something new I learned about myself is

3 Being able to share things about myself with another person is important to me because

4 I find this difficult at times because

Useful websites

http://kidshealth.org – go to the teen health section and find helpful advice on all aspects of growing up, including self-esteem and friendships

www.barnardos.ie – the teen section offers helpful suggestions and advice on many of the challenges of growing up

Review of Unit 2: *How I See Myself and Others*

1. In this unit I learned about _____
_____
_____

2. I think that this will help me _____
_____
_____

3. I liked _____
_____
_____

4. I did not like _____
_____
_____

5. I would like to learn more about _____
_____
_____

6. This topic links with (another topic in SPHE or another subject) _____
_____
_____

UNIT 3 Being an Adolescent

KEY WORDS

Adolescence
Sexuality
Values

Learning Outcomes:

This unit helps you to:

1. Understand what it means to be an adolescent ○
2. Learn about the 'Tasks of Adolescence' ○
3. Recognise that your sexuality is an integral part of what it means to be a man or a woman. ○

(Tick off as you complete them.)

KEY WORDS

Adolescence
A phase of growth and development between childhood and adulthood.

Who Am I Now? The Tasks of Adolescence

In your SPHE classes in first and second year you have already explored the ways in which you change and grow during adolescence. It is a challenging time as you enter post-primary school as a child but leave it as an adult. That's a lot of growing up to do in five or six years!

This year you will look at other changes that happen to you during this time – changes in how you think and relate to people, in the way you feel and in your identity.

These changes are sometimes called the 'Tasks of Adolescence'. These are areas of your life that you need to work through on the journey to becoming an adult. They can be described under five main headings which sometimes overlap.

Physical

- Growing rapidly
- Developing sexually.

Identity

- Wanting to be different from your family (e.g. becoming a vegetarian or developing an interest in another religion or belief system)
- Becoming ashamed of, or embarrassed by, your family
- Choosing your own friends
- Changing your name or the spelling of your name (e.g. using nicknames or pet names)
- Trying out different accents.

Body image

- Becoming preoccupied with your appearance
- Worrying about your rate of physical change
- Being critical of your appearance
- Comparing yourself with sports stars and with the celebrity 'perfect body' type as shown in the media.

I'M BEAUTIFUL AND I KNOW IT

· BODY POSITIVE ·

Did You Know?

The world's tallest teenager, Broc Brown, is a record-breaking 7 feet 8 inches tall and he's still growing!

Autonomy

- Desiring independence from your family
- Making your own decisions
- Challenging authority – in your school and/or with your parents/carers
- Wanting privacy
- Feeling alone and lonely
- Arguing and breaking rules.

Intellectual

- Moving to abstract thought and starting to think about things more deeply and reason things out for yourself
- Thinking about what's possible in your own life
- Becoming self-absorbed and idealistic
- Beginning to understand the importance of consequences
- Wanting to be included in adult conversations
- Deciding that a growing list of things are now childish.

Growing up doesn't just happen overnight. It's a journey and takes time, so be patient with yourself!

1   The four questions of adolescence

There are four questions that sum up what most young people are concerned about at this time in their lives.

1. **Who am I?** Many teenagers worry about what kind of person they are and about their uniqueness.

2. **Am I normal?** Being 'normal' depends on who you are, your personality, your interests, your likes and dislikes, hopes for the future and so on.

3. **Am I competent?** Being competent means having a 'can do' attitude and being able to take responsibility for yourself.

4. **Am I lovable and loving?** Being able to love others and allow yourself to be loved and appreciated by other people and understanding and appreciating everything that goes with that.

These four questions are written on the brick wall below. On the bricks beside each question, write what you think it means. One of the questions, 'Am I normal?', is done for you. Add anything else that you think this question could mean and answer the other three questions.

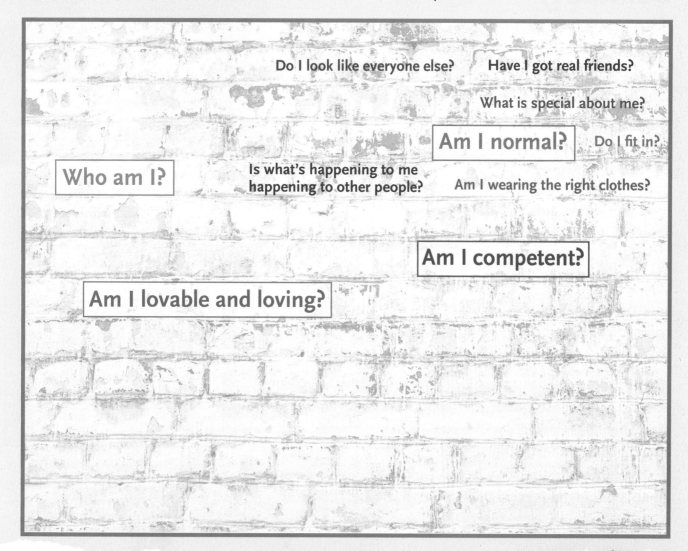

1. Share your work with the class and then have a discussion to decide which of the four questions of adolescence your class think causes the most worry and anxiety for young people.

2. What would help young people to work out answers to the questions on your wall?

After learning about the four questions of adolescence the question that concerns me most is

This is because

I can get support or help with this, if I need it, by

Sexuality

In Activity 1 you may have come up with all sorts of questions about who you are at this stage of your life. While everybody is unique and different, people often have the same concerns and questions about growing up. These questions may cause anxiety and worry at times. One area which can be particularly confusing for young people is their sexuality. You will hear about sexuality in the media, in the lyrics of songs, and in films, box sets and so on, but people rarely have an open discussion about it, so it is easy to get confused about what sexuality means.

KEY WORDS

Sexuality

An important part of each person, it includes the feelings, thoughts and behaviours associated with being male or female, who we are attracted to, romantically and otherwise, and being in love and in relationships that include sexual intimacy and sexual activity. It also includes the human dimensions of reproduction and pregnancy.

Your sexuality

Your sexuality is a normal, positive and lifelong part of you and it contributes to your overall health and wellbeing. It is an important part of who we all are as human beings.

Many factors influence your sexuality and your attitudes towards your sexuality. These include your self-esteem, your family and society and the messages you receive growing up. Your knowledge, attitudes and values also influence it. Other influences may be cultural, spiritual or ethically based. It is easy to understand why this is a complex topic!

People often think that their sexuality has only to do with their body parts and sex but it is about a lot more than that. Your sexuality is about you as a whole person. Below are some of the components of sexuality, some of which you have already explored in previous SPHE classes, and some of which you will explore later in Strand 3.

Aspects of your sexuality

- **Gender identity:** Your sense of being male or female

- **Gender role:** How you behave or are expected to behave as a male or female

- **Sexual orientation:** Who you are attracted to, romantically and sexually

- **Your body and body image:** The different parts of your body and how you think and feel about your body; the ways in which your feelings about your body affect your relationships; how you dress; how you look after your body and take care of your sexual health

- **Communication, relationships and intimacy:** How you communicate in relationships and understanding what makes a relationship healthy or unhealthy; beginning, maintaining and ending relationships; being emotionally close to someone in a loving, caring relationship and learning about intimacy; being in a sexual relationship

- **Values, beliefs and influences:** Influences of family, friends, religion, culture, society and the media, and how these affect the way you think and feel about your sexuality.

You will learn more about this topic in Strand 3.

Assessment – Check your learning

Adolescence is the journey from childhood to adulthood. It is a challenging time and for some teenagers it can be a difficult time. Look at what you wrote on the wall in Activity 1. Use these points, along with some additional research online or in the library, to write a more detailed response to each of the four questions, giving four tips that might help a young person to stay on course as they make their way along this journey. Keep your work in your SPHE folder or e-folder.

Activity 2

What shapes you?

You may not be aware of the things that influence you or of the messages you receive that affect how you think, feel and behave. With two others, brainstorm the different messages you received growing up for each of the different aspects of sexuality outlined on the right. These messages can be from parents, family, friends, your school, the media, your culture or your church.

Write them on the relevant parts of the body outline. As your teacher takes feedback from the rest of the class add in any new ideas. Then answer the questions and complete your Learning Log.

Values, beliefs and influences:

Human sexuality:

Gender identity and gender roles:

Sexual orientation:

Your body and body image:

Communication, relationships and intimacy:

1 How might messages that young people receive about aspects of sexuality affect them in their lives generally and in their relationships?

_____

_____

_____

2 If there are boys and girls in your class write down some differences between the messages that boys and girls get and how you think this might affect their attitudes to sexuality and relationships.

_____

_____

_____

_____

KEY WORDS

Values

Beliefs about what is important in your life and what guides your behaviour.

LEARNING LOG

1 Three new things I now know about sexuality are

_____

2 Three things about sexuality that I found easiest to talk about were

_____

because

_____

3 The three things that I found it most difficult to talk about were

_____

because

_____

4 I can get help with any concerns about my sexuality by

_____

Useful Websites

www.barnardos.ie – working with vulnerable children and their families; the teen help section offers invaluable advice and support for young people

http://kidshealth.org – great advice and tips on how to deal with being a teenager

Review of Unit 3: *Being an Adolescent*

1. In this unit I learned about _____

_____

_____

2. I think that this will help me _____

_____

_____

3. I liked _____

_____

_____

4. I did not like _____

_____

_____

5. I would like to learn more about _____

_____

_____

6. This topic links with (another topic in SPHE or another subject) _____

_____

_____

Minding Myself and Others

UNIT 1 Being Healthy

Learning Outcomes:

This unit helps you to:

1. Discover your rights as a young person ○
2. Become aware of what is meant by child abuse ○
3. Understand the effects of living with abuse ○
4. Find out where to go for help or more information on the topic. ○

(Tick off as you complete them.)

Appropriate Care Giving and Receiving

In earlier units you learned about keeping your body healthy by eating well, being active and getting enough sleep. You learned about self-esteem and wellbeing and the importance of being part of a community.

In this final unit in the 'Being Healthy' strand you are going to learn about a very important issue – children's rights.

All children have rights. The United Nations Convention on the Rights of the Child (1990) is an agreement that lists all the rights that young people under the age of eighteen are entitled to. Ireland has signed up to working towards granting these rights. This is done by basing Irish laws on these rights.

> **KEY WORDS**
>
> A right
> Child abuse
> Significant harm

> **KEY WORDS**
>
> **A right**
> A moral or legal entitlement to do or have something.

> You can read about children's rights, in simple language, on www.itsyourright.ie. You can get the official version on www.childrensrights.ie, under Children's Rights.

The UN rights are set out in Articles. Let's look at some of them:  PowerPoint

You have the right:

To know your rights (Article 42)

To live with your parents unless it is bad for you (Article 9)

To be free from sexual abuse (Article 34)

To an education (Article 28)

To play and rest (Article 31)

To be protected from all types of abuse and neglect (Article 19)

To food, clothing, a safe place to live and have your basic needs met (Article 27)

To give your opinion and have it taken into account in any matter concerning you (Article 12)

To protection from any type of exploitation (Article 36)

To not be punished in a cruel or harmful way (Article 37)

To protection from work that harms you, and is bad for your health and education (Article 32)

Activity 1

Your rights – what's important to you

Think carefully about the rights of the child as listed above.

1 Pick out the three rights you feel are the most important and list them below.

1 _____

2 _____

3 _____

2 In a small group talk about the three rights each of you chose and agree on which three you think are the most important. Write them at the top of page 49.

1 _____

2 _____

3 _____

3 Why did your group choose those three rights?

1 _____

_____

_____

2 _____

_____

_____

CHARTER

This class believes that every child has the right to;

_____

_____

_____

_____

_____

As a class, discuss your choices. Putting them all together, come up with **one** sentence that best sums up the rights every child should have and write it into the 'Charter' on the right.

The History of Children's Rights

In Europe the idea of children having rights is a relatively new concept. In the 1800s and during Victorian times in the British Empire children were supposed to be 'seen and not heard'. During the industrial revolution some children worked in mines and factories and child mortality (the death rate among children) was much higher than it is today. In some English city slums 50 per cent of children died in their first year and one in three died before the age of five. Today, in Ireland, fewer than 1 in 200 children die.

There are many Irish laws that protect young people's rights. For example, if you are aged fourteen or fifteen you can get a job doing light work during the school holidays, but you must have at least twenty-one days off work during this time.

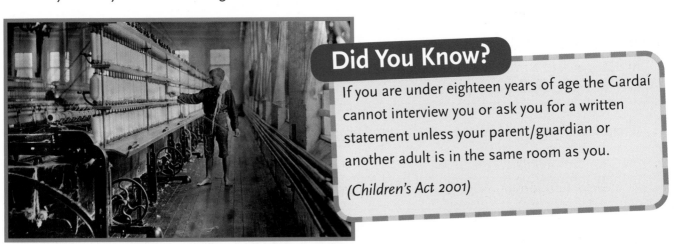

Did You Know?

If you are under eighteen years of age the Gardaí cannot interview you or ask you for a written statement unless your parent/guardian or another adult is in the same room as you.

(Children's Act 2001)

Activity 2

Right or wrong?

Read the statements below about the rights of the child and decide if you agree or disagree with the person's behaviour or if you are unsure if it is right or wrong. Mark your answers in the grid below.

When your teacher reads out each statement, hold up one of the traffic light pages at the back of your textbook to show your answer – hold up green if you agree, red if you disagree or orange if you are unsure. You must be able to explain why you made your decision and, if possible, persuade other people in your class to change their minds.

Statement		Agree	Disagree	Unsure
		Green	Red	Orange
1	When they go to the pub at night parents lock their children, aged six, eight and ten, into their bedrooms.			
2	Father has a hard tackle with his eleven-year-old son while they are playing soccer and accidentally breaks his arm.			
3	Parents constantly fight in front of their children, swearing and occasionally throwing things at each other.			
4	Toddler repeatedly throws her soother onto the floor and her father gives it back to her each time. Eventually he smacks her on the hand.			
5	A childminder who is drunk collects a child from school and drives home.			
6	A single parent works night shifts and leaves a twelve-year-old and a fourteen-year-old home alone.			
7	A fifteen-year-old works all summer on the family farm to make money for the school ski trip.			
8	Parents do not speak to their fifteen-year-old for a week after disappointing mock exam results.			
9	Parents allow their fourteen-year-old to miss school any time he says he feels unwell. Child has missed forty-two days this year.			
10	Grandmother accidently spills hot oil on her grandchild, burning her badly.			
11	Scout leader puts thirteen-year-old standing outside the tent for 15 minutes at 1.30 a.m. because she was messing and keeping everyone else awake.			

1 What helped you to decide where you stand on each of these issues?

_____

2 Is there information that you do not have that you feel would help you to make your decision?

_____

Your teacher will give you background information on these issues.

One thing I learned about the rights of children that I think is positive is

Child Abuse and Child Protection

In the past, what is now seen as child abuse was often accepted as normal behaviour. You may have heard the expression 'spare the rod and spoil the child'. It meant that if parents did not physically punish their child's misbehaviour the child would become a spoilt brat!

In 1783, Poland was the first country to outlaw corporal punishment (slapping and beating children) in schools. Most developed countries have now banned hitting children in school. However, only thirty-one of the fifty of the states in the USA have banned it in public schools and corporal punishment is common in many African and Southeast Asian schools.

Until 1982 corporal punishment in schools was allowed in Ireland and it only became a criminal offence in 1996. The *Children First Act 2015* finally made it illegal for parents to smack their children in Ireland. Before this Act there was no clear definition of what actually was child abuse and what should be done if it happened.

This has now changed, as the *Children First Act* gives clear guidelines on what is considered child abuse. It also explains the responsibilities of everyone involved with children to protect children's rights and to report any concerns they might have that a child is being abused to **Tusla** or to **An Garda Síochána**.

So, let's see what is now regarded as child abuse.

Categories of child abuse

Child abuse is divided into four different categories:

1 Neglect   **2** Emotional abuse

3 Physical abuse   **4** Sexual abuse.

While doing any of these things to children is always wrong, for an action to be considered child abuse it must cause **significant harm** to the child. This means that it must damage the child's health or development when compared to a child of similar age. A once-off incident of sexual or physical abuse may be considered child abuse.

KEY WORDS

Child abuse

When a parent or caregiver of a person under the age of eighteen either fails to provide appropriate care or mistreats him or her. This mistreatment must cause significant harm to the child.

Significant harm

When the child's health or development is neglected so much that his/her wellbeing and/or development are severely affected.

Neglect

- To deprive a child of adequate food, clothing, warmth, hygiene, intellectual stimulation, supervision, attachment and affection of adults, safety or medical care
- Abandonment
- A child being exploited or overworked
- Ongoing failure to send a child to school.

Emotional abuse

- When the child's needs for affection, approval and security are not met
- Constant criticism, sarcasm and blaming
- Unreasonable responsibilities, discipline or expectations
- Exposure to domestic violence
- Care which is dependent on child's performance.

Physical abuse

- Severe physical punishments – bites, burns, broken bones
- Poisoning
- Terrorising with threats
- Allowing the child to observe violence
- Fabricated or induced illness in the child
- Allowing a child to be at risk or harm.

Sexual abuse

- When a child is used by someone for sexual gratification or arousal
- Sexual touching of a child
- Taking sexual images of a child
- Showing sexually explicit material to a child
- Sexual exploitation of a child.

Living with abuse can affect the way you think. An abused child can feel:

Rejected · TRAPPED · Ashamed · Worthless · Helpless · Dirty · Afraid · Stupid · Guilty · Confused · Angry · Useless

Did You Know?

Internationally 20 per cent of women and 5–10 per cent of men report that they were sexually abused as children.

(Ark of Hope for Children 2017)

Remember

Abuse is NEVER your fault.

Assessment – Check your learning

Knowing what you know now

Go back and read the twelve statements in Activity 2 again. List the ones that you feel are cases of child abuse and explain why you think this is the case.

_____

_____

_____

_____

_____

_____

_____

Getting Help

A problem shared is a problem halved

If you are being abused it is important that you tell a trusted adult, perhaps a family member or a teacher. No matter how awful you think your situation is there are people who will understand. They cannot keep what you tell them to themselves but they will know how to help you.

If you want more information on child abuse or getting help, check out the websites below.

Did You Know?

In 2016, Childline answered 385,673 calls and 19,582 web chats/text messages. Many young people contacted Childline to speak about being afraid of losing their home. Traveller children spoke about not feeling in control of their lives and children in residential care spoke about negative experiences, including bullying or not having a social worker.

Useful Websites

www.childline.ie – information on many teenage issues, including abuse. They have a 24-hour listening service on 1800 66 66 66 or text Talk to 50101

www.barnardos.ie – you can get more information on child abuse under resources and advice

www.samaritans.org – details on the twenty branches around Ireland where you are welcome to drop in for one-to-one help and on their 24-hour helpline that you can call for free on 116 123 or you can email jo@samaritans.org

Review of Unit 1: *Being Healthy*

1 In this unit I learned about _____

_____

_____

2 I think that this will help me _____

_____

_____

3 I liked _____

_____

_____

4 I did not like _____

_____

_____

5 I would like to learn more about _____

_____

_____

6 This topic links with (another topic in SPHE or another subject) _____

_____

_____

Minding Myself and Others

UNIT 2 Substance Use

Learning Outcomes:

This unit helps you to:

1. Understand how the main categories of drugs work on your body and mind ◯

2. Become aware of the link between substance use and mental health ◯

3. Explore the personal and social resources needed to avoid substance use problems ◯

4. Investigate what information and supports are available for young people in relation to substance use in your area. ◯

(Tick off as you complete them.)

In *Health and Wellbeing: SPHE 1* and *Health and Wellbeing: SPHE 2* you learned about the main categories of drugs and how drug use affects you, your family and society. You looked at alcohol, tobacco and cannabis in detail in first and second year. This year you will examine ecstasy, cocaine, heroin and amphetamines, discuss the pressure on people to use drugs, and the link between substance use and mental health.

KEY WORDS

Ecstasy

Cocaine

Heroin

Amphetamines

Psychoactive drugs

Polydrug use

Last year you examined the types or categories of drugs and you were introduced to the drugs heroin, cocaine and ecstasy (see *Health and Wellbeing: SPHE 2*, page 85). These are very dangerous, illegal drugs and their use can lead to severe, long-term health, financial and social problems. It is important that you know how these drugs work and how they can affect your life.

Some of you may already have information on these drugs as they are often mentioned in online and printed newspapers and magazines, in films, and on TV. Your teacher will also suggest some other sources of information that could be helpful, e.g. resources from the HSE health promotion units or websites you could use for research.

KEY WORDS

Ecstasy

A stimulant drug which makes people feel more alert and can change the way they see reality. It comes in small tablets that usually have a logo or design on them.

Cocaine

A very addictive stimulant drug that comes as a fine white powder and is usually snorted. Sometimes it is in the form of a rock crystal that is heated and the vapour is inhaled (crack cocaine).

Heroin

A highly addictive drug made from the opium poppy, it gives a feeling (rush) of calm and pleasure. It usually comes as a white or brownish powder which is injected, sniffed, snorted or smoked.

Amphetamines

An addictive group of drugs that increase brain activity, creating a feeling of exhilaration, energy and confidence. Amphetamines usually come in in a white or pinkish powder or tablets.

Activity

1

How much do you know?

 PowerPoint

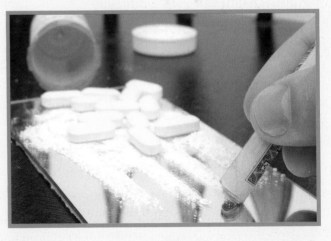

Look at the information on the cards on page 58 about five aspects of four drugs: Heroin, Ecstasy, Cocaine and Amphetamines. The aspects are: **slang names**, **how it is taken**, **short-term effects**, **long-term effects** and **signs and symptoms** that someone is using it. Write the information on each of the cards into the correct box in the Drug Information Frame on page 59. The cards relating to Ecstasy have been done for you.

Runny, itchy nose. Very rapid heartbeat. Dilated pupils. Huge energy, followed by exhaustion and sometimes confusion.

Very large pupils. Lots of energy and talkative. Sweating. Huge thirst. Jaw grinding. Jerky movements. Unable to sleep (insomnia).

Very small pupils. Slurred speech. Shallow breathing. 'Track' marks on body from using needles. Glassy eyes. Difficulty keeping awake.

Hyperactivity. Jerky movements. Very large pupils. Insomnia. Staring. Grinding of teeth.

Usually snorted up the nose. Can be injected or smoked.

Swallowed as a tablet (tab).

White, pink, grey or yellowish powder is snorted, mixed in a drink or prepared for injection.

In its pure form it can be swallowed or dissolved in water and injected into a vein. It can also be sniffed.

Speed. Uppers., Whizz. Billy. Phet. Benz. Jelly beans or super jellies. Eye openers.

Smack. Junk. Horse. China white. H. Nod. White horse. Brown sugar. Skunk.

XTC. Doves. MDMA. E. Disco biscuits. Yokes. Denis the Menace. Shamrock. Scooby Snacks.

Coke. Snow. Charlie. Blow. Flake. Soda. Fluff. Nose candy.

Feelings of euphoria and energy. Increases body temperature, blood pressure and heart rate. In rare cases sudden death can occur on first use.

Feelings of contentment, excitement and energy. Anxiety, depression and difficulty concentrating.

Feelings of increased mental and physical ability.

Reduces the effects of anxiety, fear and discomfort. The 'rush' which lasts about a minute is an intense, pleasurable high. It is followed by a feeling of peacefulness and contentment. The more you use it the harder it is to feel the intense high.

Regular use causes poor health due to lack of sleep and poor appetite. Paranoia. Hallucinations. Violent behaviour. Cravings for the drug. Compulsive drug-seeking behaviour. Convulsions. Respiratory problems. Loss of coordination. Obsessive behaviour.

Diseases such as Hepatitis A, B and C, AIDS, tetanus and blood poisoning, abscesses, inflammation of the heart and veins, clots and viral infections spread by needle sharing. Brain damage has been reported in chronic users in the US. Death from overdose.

Heatstroke. Dehydration. Headaches, fits and unexplained pains. Occasionally causes death through heart or lung failure, or brain haemorrhage.

Risk of heart attacks, respiratory failure, strokes, seizures, stomach pain and nausea. Death from overdose or from risk taking while 'high'.

Drug information frame

Drug	Slang names	How it is taken	Short-term effects	Long-term effects	Signs and symptoms of use
Ecstasy	XTC. Doves. MDMA. E. Disco Biscuits. Yokes. Denis the Menace. Shamrocks. Scooby Snacks.	Swallowed as a tablet (tab).	Feelings of contentment, excitement and energy. Anxiety, depression and difficulty concentrating.	Heatstroke. Dehydration. Headaches, fits and unexplained pains. Occasionally, causes death through heart or lung failure, or brain haemorrhage.	Very large pupils. Lots of energy and talkative. Sweating. Huge thirst. Jaw grinding. Jerky movements. Unable to sleep (insomnia).
Heroin					
Cocaine					
Amphetamines					

59

LEARNING LOG

One other fact about one of these drugs that I know is

_____

_____

For more detailed information on each of these drug types see www.drugs.ie

Did You Know?

Addiction to gambling is a growing problem in Ireland. Irish people gamble €14 million every day! Ireland has the third highest gambling losses per adult in the world and has an estimated 28,000 – 40,000 problem gamblers. Adolescent gambling is thought to be 2–3 times the rate of adults. It is estimated that 77 per cent of gambling profits are from online gambling. Gambling addiction can lead to loss of family, friends, homes and jobs and one in five problem gamblers attempt suicide.

Substance Use and Mental Health

In *Health and Wellbeing: SPHE 2* you looked at how drugs are often categorised by the effect they have and that the four main categories are:

Depressants
Slow down the work of your body and make you feel relaxed and drowsy

Stimulants
Increase physical and mental activity – they can 'pick you up'

Hallucinogens
Change how you see reality – you see and hear things differently, including things that do not exist

Opiates
Very strong painkillers; induce sleep

As you can see, all these drugs affect how your brain works. Depending on the drug, psychoactive drugs can heighten some emotions or feelings and dampen others. The most common of these drugs are alcohol, cannabis, ecstasy and heroin. Polydrug use, of for example alcohol and cannabis, is dangerous, as the effects of the psychoactive drugs are combined and can be more difficult to treat.

KEY WORDS

Psychoactive drugs

Chemical substances that alter how your brain functions, causing temporary changes to your mood, consciousness, and how you see things and behave.

Polydrug use

When two or more psychoactive drugs are used together or in quick succession.

LEARNING LOG

Two examples of how drug use affects mood, consciousness, behaviour or how we see things are:

1 _____

2 _____

Substance abuse is linked to mental health problems

You have learned how psychoactive drugs have the ability to affect your mood by interfering with the chemicals in your brain. The effects can be short term, making the drug user feel or act strangely. The effects stop when the drug wears off. Short-term effects include panic attacks, delusions, hallucinations and mood changes.

Long-term drug use has been linked to depression, schizophrenia and bipolar disorder. These mental health conditions are explained in Strand 4, Unit 2 (see page 147).

Remember

Young people appear to be significantly more at risk of mental health issues linked to drug use, especially if they have started to use drugs at an early age when their brain is still developing.

Vicious cycle of substance use and mental health issues

The link between mental health problems and substance use is a complicated one. It is not clear why some people who use drugs suffer long-term, permanent effects to their mental health and others do not. It is possible that the drug use can trigger a pre-existing, unknown mental health condition or that the drug permanently disrupts the chemical balance in the brain, leading to mental illness.

Some people with mental health issues use drugs as a way of dealing with the side effects of their medication. Other people may use drugs to cope with difficulties in their life, such as loneliness, shyness, failure or grief. This, in turn, can create more problems.

The National Survey of Youth Mental Health in Ireland (2012) found clear evidence that excessive drinking in young people is associated with poor mental health and low self-esteem. There are also strong links between excessive drinking and suicidal behaviour, as alcohol and drug use increase your likelihood to act on sudden urges, changing your mood and leading to depression. Suicide is the leading cause of death in Ireland in the 15–24 age group and alcohol is a factor in more than half of the suicides in Ireland.

Substance use can lead to, or trigger, mental health issues

Drugs and alcohol

People with mental health issues may abuse substances as a way of coping

Substance use makes pre-existing mental health issues worse

Did You Know?

People who abuse alcohol and/or drugs or are dependent on them, attempt suicide nearly six times more often than people who do not abuse these substances.

(*Drug Addiction as Risk for Suicide, NCBI 2015*)

Assessment – Check your learning

Making your point

Using the information you have learned so far organise a class debate on the motion:

For the protection of young people alcohol should be included in the list of banned drugs.

Avoiding substance use problems

Before you look at how best you can avoid having problems with alcohol or other drugs, you need to discuss the reasons why young people use drugs. If we can understand these reasons we can all work towards providing the resources needed to reduce the damage done by alcohol and drug abuse to individuals, families and society.

Some of the resources needed are personal, such as building self-confidence, good communication skills and supportive friendships. The Health and Wellbeing programme in your SPHE classes will help you to work on these. Other resources, such as providing activities for teenagers, dealing with housing planning problems and fixing the lack of opportunities for all young people to develop their talents, are the responsibility of Irish society and the community in general.

Activity 2

Circles

In the 'Reason' circles on the left, there is a list of some reasons why young people might use drugs, including alcohol. Two of the circles are empty. Working in groups of three, discuss these reasons and write any other reasons your group can think of in the two blank circles.

In the 'Rating' circles in the middle, give a rating between 1 and 10 on the reasons why you feel that young people use alcohol/drugs. Give the reason your group believe is the most significant a score of 10 and work your way down to 1. There are more than 10 circles below, so some circles will not have a score at all.

In the 'Resource/Skills needed to deal with this' circles on the right write in the resources and/or skills that you think might help to deal with some of these issues. For example, in row 1, 'Peer pressure' you might write 'Work on skills for resisting peer pressure' or after 'Boredom' you could insert, 'Take up a hobby and/or get a part-time job'.

Reason	Rating	Resources/Skills needed to deal with this
1. Peer pressure		
2. Boredom		
3. Lack of confidence and self-esteem		
4. Desire to get high		
5. Pleasure and fun		
6. Escape from reality		
7. Curiosity		
8. Poor relationship with parents		

(9) To cope with loss
     and loneliness

(10) To deal with mental
     health issues

(11) Bullied

(12)

(13)

Compare the scores your group gave for each reason with the scores of the other groups in your class and get an average class score. Then answer the questions below.

1 What are the top three reasons young people use drugs, according to your class?

Reason 1 _____

Reason 2 _____

Reason 3 _____

2 How did your class's top three reasons compare with your group's top three?

_____

_____

3 Which reason was it most difficult to come up with a resource or skill to deal with?

_____

4 What, do you think, does that tell you?

_____

_____

5 How many of the resources and/or skills needed to deal with drug use do you have in your life? List them below.

_____

_____

_____

Substance Use: Why Start?

In Activity 2 you looked at reasons why young people might start using alcohol and other drugs. In the next activity you are going to turn this on its head and come up with reasons why you shouldn't use them.

> *You see things; and you say, 'Why?' But I dream things that never were; and I say, 'Why not?'*
>
> (George Bernard Shaw)

Activity

3

Why not?

In pairs or groups of four, come up with as many reasons as you can why people might decide not to use alcohol or drugs.

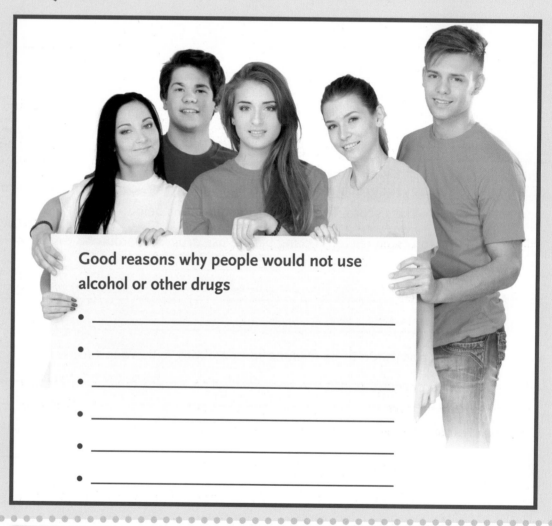

Good reasons why people would not use alcohol or other drugs

- _____
- _____
- _____
- _____
- _____
- _____

When you have shared all the lists with the class, have a discussion and agree on a single most important reason and write it here:

_____

LEARNING LOG

Activity 4
Substance use and SPHE

After doing Activity 2 and Activity 3 you will have noticed that many of the resources that help to protect against drug and alcohol abuse are ones you have already discussed in your SPHE programme. Working in pairs, think about the question below and then write your answer:

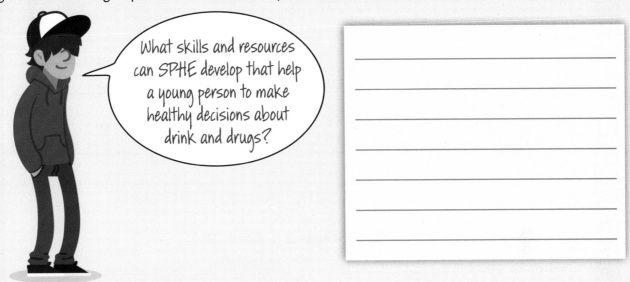

What skills and resources can SPHE develop that help a young person to make healthy decisions about drink and drugs?

Supports in My Area

If you or someone you know has a problem with alcohol or other drugs it is important to be able to find out what type of help is available in your area.

Activity 5
Help needed!

The websites below provide starting points for finding out what help is available in your locality for young people who have problems with addiction. Use them to fill in the 'Addiction Service' form on page 68. Your teacher will give you an extra form if you need one.

National directory of drugs and alcohol services

www.services.drugs.ie – choose the type of service and your county, and then search to find services in your area. Use the map search or advanced search for more detailed options

www.therisefoundation.ie – the useful links will bring you to a list of help agencies for addiction supports in Ireland

www.hse.ie – search for specialist care and addiction services to find information on support services by region

Addiction Service

Name of service: _____

Address: _____

Phone No: _____

Email: _____

Website: _____

Types of addiction dealt with: _____

Age group: _____

Male ❑   Female ❑   Both ❑

Referral: Self-Referral ❑   GP ❑   School ❑   Other ❑

Treatments offered: _____

Residential/Day centre: _____

Length of treatments: _____

Cost: _____

Health Insurance ❑   Free ❑   Loan scheme ❑   Private ❑

Comments: _____

_____

_____

_____

_____

Useful Websites

www.drugs.ie – includes drug and alcohol information, services and resources and 'Drugs info' for young people

www.problemgambling.ie – provides information on how to get help and a callback service

www.reachout.com – information on all aspects of mental health and addiction, alcohol and drugs

Assessment – Check your learning

As a class group, invite a speaker from one of the local help agencies dealing with teen addiction, or teens living with parental addiction, to visit your class. Ask them to talk to you about the service they provide and the nature of the problems they encounter. Before the visit prepare a list of questions that you would like answered by your speaker. Select a student to welcome your guest and another to thank them.

Review of Unit 2: *Substance Use*

1. In this unit I learned about _____

_____

_____

2. I think that this will help me _____

_____

_____

3. I liked _____

_____

_____

4. I did not like _____

_____

_____

5. I would like to learn more about _____

_____

_____

6. This topic links with (another topic in SPHE or another subject) _____

_____

_____

Minding Myself and Others

UNIT **3** Respectful Communication

Learning Outcomes:

This unit helps you to:

1. Be conscious of what good manners are and why they are important ○
2. Become aware of the consequences of not dealing with conflict ○
3. Have a knowledge of the main causes of conflict ○
4. Learn the skills of managing conflict ○
5. Understand which is your preferred conflict management style ○
6. Practice making 'I' statements ○
7. Apply your new skills. ○

(Tick off as you complete them.)

KEY WORDS

Etiquette

A code of polite conduct or good manners that make everyone's dealings with each other more pleasant.

Since first year you have learned a lot about communication. You should now be clear about the skills you need to be a good listener and you should know the difference between assertive, aggressive and passive communication. You are probably more aware of the huge role body language plays in your relationships and you can handle criticism without getting mortally offended. In this final unit on respectful communication

you are going to move on to one of the trickier aspects of communication – how to handle conflict! But first we will have a look at one of the aspects of behaviour and communication that makes life more pleasant for everybody – good manners or etiquette.

Knowing how you should behave in social situations will give you confidence and avoid embarrassment.

Activity 1

Mind your manners!

 PowerPoint

Study the five pictures below. Circle in red the examples that you think show bad manners. Then answer the six questions that follow and complete the Learning Log.

1 Are there any other messages about good or bad manners in the pictures?

_____

_____

_____

_____

2 What, if any, were the examples of bad manners that not everybody agreed with?

_____

_____

_____

_____

3 What other examples of bad manners have you experienced?

_____

_____

4 Think of one example of a time when you experienced bad manners or someone was rude to you. What did that person do or say?

_____

_____

5 How did it make you feel?

_____

_____

6 How did you react?

_____

_____

One reason why I think good manners are important is

_____

_____

_____

_____

LEARNING LOG

Assessment – Check your learning

Choose one of the following areas:

- Classroom
- Canteen
- Bus
- Home
- At the table

Using an A4 page, create a 'Guide to Good Manners' for the area you chose and display your work on your classroom wall. Later you can save it in your SPHE folder.

Are Good Manners dead?

Dealing with Conflict

While good manners will greatly help to reduce the conflict in your life, some friction is unavoidable. Most people are likely to have some potential for conflict in their lives every day. For example, if your mother asks you to pick up your clothes just as you're dashing out to play football or your dad won't let you play video games until you've done your homework or a classmate sits in your place and won't move, the result can be a disagreement.

KEY WORDS

Conflict

A difference or disagreement between two people.

You cannot avoid conflict, but you can learn to manage it so that it doesn't lead to tension, arguments and bad feelings. In this section, you will look at what causes conflict, how to handle it and the ways in which you can improve your conflict management skills.

KEY WORDS

Tension

A feeling of worry or anxiety when there is the possibility of conflict.

Activity 2

Sources of conflict

1. In the image of the bomb write all the things that can cause conflict or tension in the life of a student in third year.

2. Add any new suggestions from other students in your class to your list and use the information to write the three most common sources of conflict for your age group:

   (a) _____

   _____

   (b) _____

   _____

   (c) _____

   _____

Conflict spiral

If conflict is not dealt with as it occurs it can grow or spiral out of control. If this happens, more people and more issues can become involved, making the original conflict much harder to resolve.

Think of how epic conflicts follow this pattern, for example *Romeo and Juliet* and World War I. These major conflicts started because of relatively minor incidents. They grew to the point where huge numbers of people were involved, but the causes of the conflicts were largely forgotten.

PowerPoint

5 Your aim changes from just making a point to winning and hurting the other people involved

3 The issues change from one to many (e.g. you might have thought that someone was rude; now you think that he/she is mean and lazy)

4 The number of people involved grow (e.g. what began between two of you now involves your friends, your brother and so on)

2 The area of the dispute grows (you might have fallen out at school and bring this into your neighbourhood or on to the sports field)

1 Tactics change from light to heavy (you might change from sulking to rudeness to excluding someone)

Causes of conflict

You cannot sort out any conflict if you do not understand what really caused it. The main causes of conflict are **differences** in **interests, understanding, values, style, opinion**, and **competing rights**.

Activity 3

Understanding the causes

Read one example of each of the main causes of conflict in the boxes below and add an example of your own to each one.

	Causes of conflict	Example	My example
1	**Interests** The difference between what I want and what you want.	I want to relax and message my friends. You want us to go to see a family movie.	
2	**Understanding** The difference between what you understand and what I understand.	I didn't answer your texts because my parents were arguing and I was stressed out. You didn't answer my texts because you were in a mood.	
3	**Values** The difference between what is important to me and what is important to you.	I want to have fun and be happy. You want me to be a doctor.	
4	**Style** The difference between the way I do things and the way you do things.	My room is mine. It's up to me how I keep it. You want me to keep it tidy all the time even though it has nothing to do with you.	
5	**Opinion** The difference between what you think and what I think.	I think rap is music. You think it is noise.	
6	**Competing rights** The difference between your rights and my rights.	I have the right to privacy. You have the right to know where I am.	

Compare your examples with other people in your class, keeping the following questions in mind: Are you happy that you fully understand the causes of conflict? Are there some examples that you feel are in the wrong category? Why is that?

Activity 4

Getting to the bottom of it

Now that you have a clearer idea about the causes of conflict, let's see how easy it is to apply it to a typical situation.

Barry forgets to give his mum a Mother's Day card. The following afternoon he comes home from school and goes online for two hours. His mum is very angry. She calls him lazy and selfish and bans the Internet for the rest of the week.

1 What might Barry think is the cause of the conflict?

_____

2 What is likely to be the real cause of the problem?

_____

3 If Barry had come home from school and started his homework immediately what might have happened?

_____

4 Give an example of a situation you found yourself in where the real cause of the conflict was ignored and the disagreement seemed to be about something else.

_____

_____

_____

AID to managing conflict

To manage conflict, you have to be sure that you know where it's coming from. Otherwise, it will keep coming back! If people won't tell you what's bothering them, you have to guess. For lots of people this is a difficult thing to do. That's why the assertive communication techniques that you learned in *Health and Wellbeing: SPHE 2* is so important. In Activity 4, if Barry's mum had simply told him that she was disappointed that he had ignored Mother's Day it would have given him a chance to do something about it and they would have avoided the fight on Monday.

There are different ways of handling conflict. The three main ones are represented by the acronym **AID**:

- **Attack**
- **Ignore**
- **Deal with it.**

My conflict management style

Before filling in the questionnaire below, think about how you usually handle conflict:

- Do you meet it head on, all guns blazing?
- Do you try to ignore it and hope that it will go away?
- Do you try to deal with it until you have sorted it out?

Choose one style and write it in the box below.

Usually my conflict management style is:

_____

Activity 5

Conflict management style quiz

Each statement below is a way of dealing with conflict. Rate each statement on a scale of 1 to 4, after deciding **how like you** it is.

Rating scale: 1 for hardly ever, 2 for sometimes, 3 for often and 4 for always.

	Statement	Rating
1	If I ignore conflict, it will go away.	
2	I try to find solutions where both people are happy.	
3	If others are happy, I am happy.	
4	When I know I'm right I don't back down.	
5	I have no problem admitting that I may be a little to blame for conflict.	
6	When there are disagreements, I gather background information to help me to understand the arguments.	
7	When I find myself in an argument, I pull back.	
8	I fearlessly argue my case.	
9	I find conflict exciting – it's a sort of game.	
10	I try to see disagreements from both sides.	
11	I generally win arguments.	
12	I avoid arguments by keeping my mouth shut.	
13	When there is a disagreement, I prefer to discuss it rather than ignore it.	
14	Fighting with others makes me unhappy and anxious.	
15	I believe that if you give in, people take advantage of you.	

Scoring

Your teacher will tell you how to use the box below to work out if you are an Eagle, an Ostrich or an Owl!

AID Style	Statement numbers and scores	Total
Attack – Eagle		
Ignore – Ostrich		
Deal with it – Owl		

Results

1 My **usual conflict management style** (your highest score) is _____

2 My **least favourite conflict management style** (lowest score) is _____

The three AID conflict management styles – Eagles, Ostriches and Owls

The fifteen statements in Activity 5 relate to the three most common ways of handling conflict: ignoring it, dealing with it and fighting about it. Many people have a style they usually use, but sometimes, in different situations, they have to use another conflict management style. For example, if your usual style is to fight, you might not do this if the conflict is with a teacher, as being aggressive would cause more trouble.

The Eagle (Attack)

Eagles force others to do things their way. They don't care about the feelings of others. They think sorting things out is more important than how people feel. Eagles can be loud and bossy. This style of conflict management is good when there is an emergency and a decision needs to be made, or when the issue is unimportant.

The Ostrich (Ignore)

Ostriches put their heads in the sand and ignore what is happening. They want a quiet life and for others to like them. They put keeping everyone happy ahead of their own needs. This conflict management style works when used at an event such as a family reunion or a family Christmas. However, ignoring the conflict in the long term means it will get worse rather than better.

The Owl (Deal with it)

Owls try to find the cause of conflict and work out a solution. They listen to the people involved and try to see the situation from other viewpoints. This style works well if the people involved must continue to work or live together. It may not be the best style, however, when time is short or the issues are unimportant.

Activity

6

Now that you have more information on the three conflict management styles, do you feel that your conflict management style score in Activity 5 is accurate? Why do you think this?

_____

_____

Activity

7

A story with three endings

Read the story and then, in groups of three, write the ending using one of the three AID styles: Attack, Ignore or Deal with it. Your teacher will tell you which style to use.

When Kevin was packing his football gear for a match, he couldn't find his sports bag. He had only two minutes before he had to leave, so he asked his sister, Aoife, for a loan of her bag. She didn't want to lend it, as she is fussy about her things and Kevin can be messy. After Kevin pleaded and the car waiting for him started beeping, she gave in and let him borrow it.

Later that week, Aoife needed her sports bag for her gym things but could not find it anywhere. Eventually she discovered it, stuffed under the stairs. Kevin's dirty football boots were still in it and the zip was broken. By the time Kevin got back from his friend's house that evening Aoife was furious.

Our ending: _____

_____

_____

After each group has read out their ending, answer the questions below.

1 How did you identify each of the three ways of managing conflict?

_____

2 Which way of dealing with conflict do you think worked best in the short term and then in the long term? _____

_____

3 Are there differences between how you deal with conflict with members of your family and with other people? _____

4 What are these differences? _____

_____

_____

From thinking about the conflict management style that I mostly use, I have learned that

An approach to managing conflict

 **PowerPoint**

By now it should be clear that if you want to have good-quality, long-term relationships in your life it is better to recognise and manage conflict before it grows into something bigger and more difficult to deal with. This is not as difficult as it might seem.

Six helpful steps

Imagine that you have decided to manage some conflict in your life by talking to the other person involved, instead of ignoring it or falling out with that person. Look at the six steps you can take to do this.

Step six: Both of you must agree to keep to the new plan of action.

Step five: Plan how you are going to put your solution into action.

Step four: Pick the solution that is fairest to both of you.

Step three: Look at all the possible ways you could resolve the conflict and the likely results of each of them.

Step two: Be clear about the problem, from both points of view. Say it in a sentence beginning with 'I' (see page 80).

Step one: Take time to calm down.

'I' statements

'I' statements (saying things in sentences beginning with 'I') are a useful way of dealing with problems without seeming to attack or to blame the other person. You simply say what is happening and how it makes you feel. For example, if your friend is late all the time, instead of saying, 'You're always late', you say, 'I get really annoyed when you keep me waiting.'

Another example would be if your brother or sister eats all the cereal even though he/she knows you haven't had your breakfast. Instead of saying, 'You are the most selfish person I know!' try saying, 'There is no cereal left and I get a headache by break time if I haven't had breakfast. I feel angry when you don't leave some for me.'

In an 'I' statement, you describe the action or the person; you don't label it (e.g. mean, stupid). This makes it easier to deal with the conflict and for both people involved to move on.

It's even better if you can use 'I' statements to clearly say what you need the other person(s) to do. For example, if the student sitting beside you keeps coughing into your work you could say, 'I feel I'm going to pick up your cold when you cough on top of me. It would be better if you'd cover your mouth and nose with a tissue when you cough.'

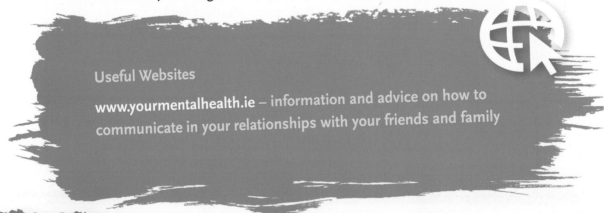

Useful Websites

www.yourmentalhealth.ie – information and advice on how to communicate in your relationships with your friends and family

Activity

8 Making 'I' statements

Write an 'I' statement for each of the situations below. Remember to explain how it makes you feel and what can be done to improve or change this.

1 Your pals arrange a trip to the cinema and don't tell you.

_____

_____

_____

2 Your sister is sulking and won't talk to you, but you don't know what you have done.

_____

_____

3 Your friend borrows your calculator and returns it broken.

_____

_____

4 Your mother gives money to your brother for washing the car, but makes you do jobs for nothing.

_____

_____

Assessment – Check your learning

 **Animation**

Cian got a part-time job in the local petrol station. He's going to be working each evening from 5.00 p.m. to 6.30 p.m. He has to help customers to put their coal or briquettes into their cars, get water for their windscreens, keep the forecourt tidy and help around the place.

One evening, while Cian was tidying the gas cylinders, Mr Fleming, his boss, shouted at him: 'Hey, Cian, come over here and help Mrs Grealish with her petrol.'

Cian rushed to do it and knocked over the flower stand beside the shop door. Mr Fleming glared at him.

Two evenings later, Cian was watching out for anyone who might need help when his boss shouted at him again: 'What are you standing around doing nothing for? Can't you see that this bag of coal is open and has made a mess of the forecourt?'

Help Cian to go through the six steps he needs to use to sort out this conflict.

PowerPoint

Step one: Take time to calm down.

Cian: _____

_____

Step two: Be clear about the problem. Say it in an 'I' statement.

Cian says: _____

Step three: Look at all your choices, name them under Cian's choice A/B/C and list the possible results of each one.

Choice	Consequence
Cian's choice A	
Cian's choice B	
Cian's choice C	

Step four: Pick the solution that is fairest to both of you.

Which one, do you think, should Cian pick and why? _____

_____

_____

Step five: Plan how you are going to put your solution into action.

Cian is going to have to _____

_____

_____

Step six: Both of you must agree to the plan.

It's not going to work if Mr Fleming does not get something out of it also. Mr Fleming will get the following out of it: _____

_____

_____

To improve my negotiation skills I need to _____

_____

_____

_____

_____

LEARNING LOG

Review of Unit 3: *Respectful Communication*

1 In this unit I learned about _____

_____

_____

2 I think that this will help me _____

_____

_____

3 I liked _____

_____

_____

4 I did not like _____

_____

_____

5 I would like to learn more about _____

_____

_____

6 This topic links with (another topic in SPHE or another subject) _____

_____

_____

Minding Myself and Others

Learning Outcomes:

This unit helps you to:

1. Learn what sexting means
2. Understand the dangers of sexting
3. Recognise the link between sexting and cyberbullying.

(Tick off as you complete them.)

KEY WORDS

Sexting
Nude selfie
Pornography
Sextortion
Revenge porn

Sexting

Over the last two years you have learned about the different types of bullying and particularly about cyberbullying. This is a new and dangerous area of bullying as it is difficult to guard against and young people can be very upset by how they are treated online. In this unit you are going to look at another online activity that can have very dangerous and damaging results for young people – sexting.

KEY WORDS

Sexting

Creating and sending sexual messages, images or videos using mobile phones, apps, social networking sites (such as Snapchat, Facebook, Viber and WhatsApp) and the Internet.

14-year-old boy added to criminal database because of naked Snapchat photo

The boy sent a naked photo of himself to a girl the same age

and she sent it to another teen in their school.

Journal.ie, 2015

Teens warned of 'dangers of sexting' by judge after girl, 14, forced into sending explicit images

███████████ persuaded his 'very vulnerable' victim to send him sexual pictures of herself using

Snapchat and then blackmailed her to send more.

Irish Mirror, 2016

Former New York congressman ███████████ **has tearfully pleaded guilty to sending obscene material to a minor**

BBC News 2016

Sexting and young people

You regularly read about people, young and not so young, such as the people in the newspaper articles above, who make the headlines because of sexting. It has become a popular activity, mainly because of the increase in the use of smartphones. In a 2013 study by the University of Utah, USA, 20 per cent of 14–18-year-old students reported that they had sent a sexual image of themselves using a mobile phone. Over twice as many students said that they had received sexual images and more than 25 per cent had forwarded those images to others. It is important that you understand the possible implications of sexting. Let's explore this further in the activities on the following pages.

KEY WORDS

Nude selfie

A commonly used term for a naked photo you take of yourself, using a mobile phone.

Did You Know?

According to a recent report, *Net Children Go Mobile 2013–2014*, 22 per cent of Irish 15–16-year-olds reported having received sexual images or messages during the previous 12 months.

Activity 1

Why do people sext?

There are many reasons why people, particularly young people, might send explicit pictures of themselves to other people. List as many of these reasons as you can think of in the screen below.

When everyone is finished share your lists and if your classmates come up with any other reasons why people sext, add them to your list.

Activity 2

What's the harm?

In the spider diagram on the next page write all the reasons why you think that sexting is a bad idea. If you can come up with more than six reasons add extra circles.

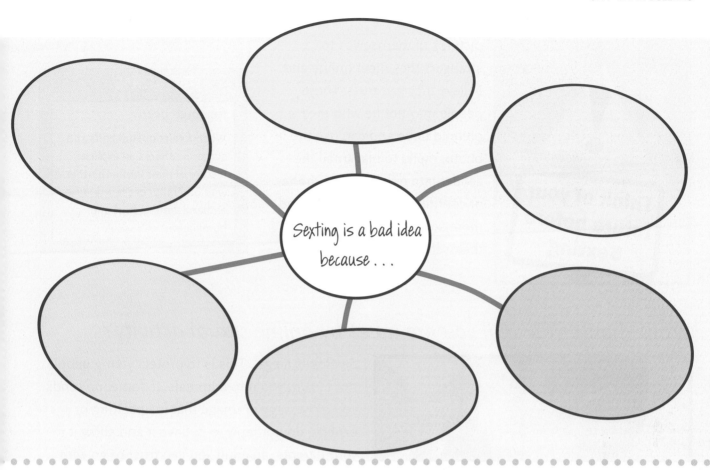

Sexting is a bad idea because . . .

The Law

The *Child Trafficking and Pornography Act 1998* makes it illegal to create, share, send, receive or store sexual images of any person under eighteen years of age. Sexual images mean pictures of the genital area or of a person engaged in a sexual act.

Under the terms of the Act, nude selfies could be categorised as pornography. The punishments for breaking this law include fines, imprisonment and getting your name added to the Register of Sex Offenders for a number of years.

Most young people do not sext. However, there have been cases where sexting has had very serious consequences, leading to bullying, sextortion or revenge porn.

You will remember from learning about cyberbullying in first and second year that if you send something online it goes out of your control and it can exist for ever. The person who receives it can save it (even Snapchat can be saved by making a screengrab of it) and share it with others. For example, if you send private pictures of yourself to someone you trust and later they are angry with you or want to get back at you for some reason, they can share pictures with other people. This is called revenge porn.

Sometimes people can be tricked into sending private

You can get more information on sexting and the law in Ireland on www.watchyourspace.ie

KEY WORDS

Pornography

Sexually explicit descriptions of naked people or sexual acts in books, pictures and other media for the purpose of sexual arousal.

Sextortion

Where someone is tricked into sending intimate pictures of themselves to someone who then uses the images to blackmail them for money or to send more images.

pictures of themselves to strangers they meet online and believe they can trust. These people may not be who they pretend to be and can use the photographs to blackmail the sender into either paying money or continuing to send more and more sexual photographs of themselves. This is sextortion.

What should you do if you are upset by online sexual activity?

Sexting is illegal. This is to protect young people, not to turn you into criminals. If someone sends you a message or image that is upsetting or explicit, do not reply to it. Save it and show it to your parents, an adult you can trust or go with them and show it to the Gardaí.

If the material is on the Internet, you can report it to the site on which it appears. Most social media sites have a 'Report' button.

Three things I learned about sexting in this class are:

1

2

3

LEARNING LOG

88

Useful Websites

www.hotline.ie – provides an anonymous facility for Internet users to report suspected illegal content, particularly child sexual abuse material, in a secure and confidential way if you accidentally encounter it online. It is run in collaboration with An Garda Síochána and is overseen by the Department of Justice and Equality and the Office for Internet Safety

www.watchyourspace.ie – a really useful site for young people who may have questions about sextortion or revenge porn

Assessment – Check your learning

Write the script

Watch 'Exposed' by CEOP (Child Exploitation and Online Protection Centre) (your teacher will give you the weblink).

With two others, write a short script of the conversation Dee has that evening when she gets home and decides to tell her parents what has happened. Your teacher will choose a group to perform their script.

Review of Unit 4: *Anti-Bullying*

1 In this unit I learned about _____

_____

_____

2 I think that this will help me _____

_____

_____

3 I liked _____

_____

_____

4 I did not like _____

_____

_____

5 I would like to learn more about _____

_____

_____

6 This topic links with (another topic in SPHE or another subject) _____

_____

_____

UNIT **1** Having a Friend and Being a Friend

Learning Outcomes:

This unit helps you to:

1. Appreciate that relationships change over time ○
2. Learn about romantic relationships ○
3. Identify qualities and/or values that are important in a healthy romantic relationship, and what makes for an unhealthy relationship ○
4. Reflect on your own values and what you want in a romantic relationship. ○

(Tick off as you complete them.)

KEY WORDS

Romantic relationship

Romantic love

Commitment

Healthy romantic relationship

Unhealthy romantic relationship

Boyfriends, Girlfriends and Romantic Relationships

Take a few minutes to think about the friends that you have had, at various stages in your life. You will see that a lot has changed in your friendships! As a child your friends were the people you played with, but as you grew up your friends were the ones you related to on a more personal level. You have already explored the changing nature of friendships and know that close friends are the friends with whom you share interests and ideas; you all have similar thoughts, feelings and values about what's important.

Friendships continue to change as you grow through adolescence. Your need for closeness and intimacy with another person increases. This closeness is found in same-sex and opposite-sex friendships and relationships that you form during these years.

Through these close relationships you continue to learn more about yourself as a person, and you also learn more about others. You also explore and come to understand what you value in a relationship. Having a boyfriend or girlfriend can be exciting, but it can also bring with it pain and hurt when things don't work out. The activities below will help you to explore this idea a little more.

Activity

1

Can boys and girls be 'just friends'?

Read the quotes below from teenagers on whether or not boys and girls can be friends. Discuss each quote with a partner and decide whether you think they are true, sometimes true or false. Circle your response. Write your answers at the end and then complete the Learning Log.

Robbie

Sally

> I think boys and girls can be friends if they want to. What's the big deal? It's not like you're going to date everyone you meet. Anyway, I think some guys are too immature to have as more than a friend.

True ☐
Sometimes true ☐
False ☐

True ☐
Sometimes true ☐
False ☐

> It just doesn't work! Boys and girls live such different lives they can't relate to each other. Boys are into sport, having a laugh with the lads and messing. Girls are gossips and you never know where you stand or what they are thinking. I can see why a girl might want to be friends with a guy because half the time they don't trust their friends.

Emily

> Why do people make such a big thing out of this? It is possible to be friends with some boys and not possible with others – it's that simple. We are all individuals and all different. It's not fair to group all boys together or all girls together. Friends come in all ages, shapes, sizes, colours and genders. That's life!

True ☐
Sometimes true ☐
False ☐

Lucy

I think boys are hard to understand. They can't be serious for one minute. They just hang around with each other laughing at nothing. Sometimes it's OK to spend time with a boy on his own but when he's with his mates it's a different story. I'd prefer to spend time with girls.

True ☐
Sometimes true ☐
False ☐

Jack

If you tell something to a girl she'll tell her friends. Also, I hate the way they rabbit on about their feelings all the time. They should lighten up. Guys never sulk or fall out with you and they don't hold grudges.

True ☐
Sometimes true ☐
False ☐

Paddy

The thing about girls is once you get friendly with them they want to go out with you. Sometimes that's not what you want. You might go out with them later but why can't you just be friends without that pressure?

True ☐
Sometimes true ☐
False ☐

Vlad

What's the big deal? I've been friends with Zita since we were in second class. We do loads of things together and have great fun. I can tell her things that I couldn't ever tell the guys and she doesn't slag me off like some of them would. It's the same for her.

True ☐
Sometimes true ☐
False ☐

Listen to the opinions of other people in your class. What effect, do you think, does making 'black and white' statements about boys and girls have on relationships between them?

_____

_____

_____

_____

Write what you think about having boys and girls as friends below.

More than just friends – romantic relationships

KEY WORDS

Romantic relationship

A close, mutually respectful relationship which includes expressions of physical affection and intimacy, ranging from holding hands, hugging and kissing to sexual intercourse.

Romantic love

A strong feeling of affection which may include physical and sexual attraction.

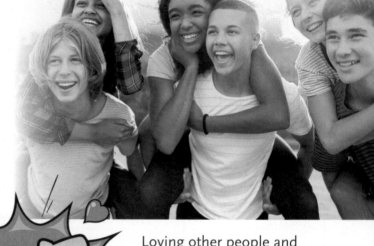

Loving other people and being loved is a basic human need. It makes us better people and makes our lives richer. By now you will have experienced love in many different ways. As a baby, you were loved by your parents/guardians, caregivers and extended family. As your friendships developed and grew you experienced other kinds of love from your close friends.

Romantic love is a different type of love from the love you feel towards a parent/guardian, a brother or sister, or even towards a close friend. This type of love is the emotion that a couple who are committed to each other share and experience. To each person in the relationship their partner is the most important person in the world! It's the same whether you are in a gay or straight relationship.

Did You Know?

Penguins are romantic. When a male penguin falls in love with a female penguin, he searches the beach to find the perfect pebble to give to her.

KEY WORDS

Commitment

A willingness or promise to give time and energy to your relationship, through all its ups and downs, because you believe in it and value it.

Healthy romantic relationship

When two people develop a connection based on shared values of trust, honesty, accountability, safety, co-operation, and support.

Adolescence is a time of change and it is at this time that you may first experience intense feelings of romantic love. It can be an exciting but also a confusing time. You might feel attracted to another person in a way that makes you want to be closer to them, both emotionally and physically. This closeness enables a special bond to grow between you and your boyfriend/girlfriend. You feel accepted and understood for who you are, and the way you are, without any need to try and be someone else. Feelings like these give you a sense of commitment to the relationship. The ingredients which contribute to a healthy romantic relationship are similar to those for any other close relationship, with one difference – a romantic relationship usually includes expressions of physical love. These range from holding hands to hugging, to kissing, and may progress to sexual intercourse.

Ingredients of a healthy relationship

Activity 2

Respect yourself

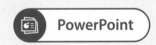
PowerPoint

Think about what you learned about healthy and unhealthy friendships in *Health and Wellbeing: SPHE 1* and *Health and Wellbeing: SPHE 2*. Then look at the 'Healthy romantic relationships wheel' on page 96, where six different qualities and values of a healthy romantic relationship are shown.

Healthy romantic relationship wheel

Trust
- Believe your partner is honest and sincere
- Be confident that they won't harm you or your relationship with them in any way.

Equality and cooperation
- Make decisions together
- Be able to say how you feel and what you think
- Acknowledge each other's interests and hobbies, even when they are different
- Be able to ask for what you want without fear
- Be prepared to share.

Responsibility
- Be willing to accept responsibility for what you say and do
- Admit to making mistakes.

Healthy romantic relationships – what do you value?

Honesty
- Be truthful and open in the way you communicate
- Be clear about what you want to say.

Support
- Be understanding and empathetic during ups and downs
- Support each other's decisions and choices
- Be prepared to listen without making a judgement.

Safety
- Don't exert power and control
- Respect your partner's boundaries
- Never use violence.

1. In pairs, discuss what you understand by each quality and/or value.
2. Complete the table below, giving an example of how each quality or value is shown in a healthy and an unhealthy romantic relationship.

Quality/Value	Healthy romantic relationship	Unhealthy romantic relationship
Honesty	You can say how you feel without fear of being judged	Refuses to be open with you about things affecting your relationship
Equality and Cooperation		
Trust		

Responsibility		
Safety		
Support		

From the qualities or values presented in the wheel I think the three most important qualities or values of a romantic relationship are

These qualities or values are important to me because

Assessment – Check your learning

Design a questionnaire which would help young people explore a relationship and decide whether it was a healthy relationship or an unhealthy one. It should have at least ten questions addressing all the different aspects of relationships that you explored in SPHE class. As a class, decide on the 10 best 'tips' from all the posters and post it on the SPHE noticeboard in your school.

www.sciencebuddies.org – good advice on making a questionnaire

Useful Websites

http://kidshealth.org – the teen health section offers helpful advice and information on all aspects of growing up, including relationships

www.b4udecide.ie – aims to encourage young people to make healthy, responsible decisions about relationships and sexual health

Review of Unit 1: *Having a Friend and Being a Friend*

1 In this unit I learned about _____

_____

_____

2 I think that this will help me _____

_____

_____

3 I liked _____

_____

_____

4 I did not like _____

_____

_____

5 I would like to learn more about _____

_____

_____

6 This topic links with (another topic in SPHE or another subject) _____

_____

_____

UNIT 2 The Relationship Spectrum

Learning Outcomes:

This unit helps you to:

1 Analyse some of the relationship difficulties experienced by young people ◯

2 Identify possible warning signs of an unhealthy or abusive relationship ◯

3 Practise some skills for ending a relationship respectfully ◯

4 Understand how to stay safe while you are dating or in a relationship. ◯

(Tick off as you complete them.)

KEY WORDS

Abuse

Respect in relationships

Relationship date

Advice

Relationship Difficulties

You have explored some of the characteristics and values that an ideal healthy relationship should have. However, we are all human and very often it's a challenge to live up to our ideals. Many of your relationships may fall short of these ideals, but you might value the relationships enough to try to make them work.

It's not always easy to see what's going on in a relationship. Sometimes you are happy with what's going on and sometimes you are not. If you are unhappy, you hope and think things will change. Sometimes they do and sometimes they don't. In Activity 1, we will look at some alarm bells that might let you know that your relationship could be in trouble.

Activity

1 Alarm bells ringing

As your teacher reads out the different situations that someone in a relationship might experience, hold up your green, red or orange traffic light page at the back of your textbook to show what you think. Choose green if you agree that the situation should start alarm bells ringing, red if you disagree and orange if you are unsure.

Remember

These situations can occur whether you are in a straight or LGBT relationship.

 PowerPoint

Statement: Is it a cause for concern that your boyfriend/girlfriend:	Agree	Disagree	Unsure
	Green	Red	Orange
1 Gets on with your close friends and family.			
2 Makes decisions without asking you.			
3 Compliments you from time to time.			
4 Makes you feel guilty if you have other interests.			
5 Respects your ideas and opinions.			
6 Accuses you of seeing someone else behind his/her back, when you did nothing.			
7 Asks you repeatedly to send sext messages to him/her.			
8 Puts you down and dismisses you.			
9 Talks to you about his/her feelings.			
10 Makes you feel unsure about your feelings for him/her.			
11 Asks you to account for what you did when you were not with him/her.			
12 Is happy for you when you get good news.			
13 Pressurises you to do things you aren't happy or comfortable doing.			
14 Loses their temper and sometimes hits you when things go wrong.			
15 Is there for you when times are tough or you are sad.			

Is your relationship working?

You have already explored some of the qualities of healthy and safe friendships and romantic relationships. These relationships are based on foundations of respect, communication, trust and similar values, where each person feels free to be themselves.

Friendships change over time and romantic relationships are no different. Usually a relationship will start out in a flurry of excitement and fun. However, as the relationship moves on there may be upsets and disagreement, sometimes leading to conflict and a breakdown in communication. Often, with some give and take and respect and understanding on both sides, these difficulties can be overcome and the relationship moves on. Sometimes, however, this is not possible and the difficulties may lead to anger, aggression and occasionally to violence and abuse. You may still feel you love the other person, but is it a good idea for you to continue in the relationship? Let's explore what you can do if this happens.

> **KEY WORDS**
>
> **Relationship date**
>
> A time, either at the beginning or during a romantic relationship, when two people meet socially. A date might also refer to the person you are meeting up with.

> **Remember**
>
> **Sexting**
> Creating and sending sexual messages, images or videos using mobile phones, apps, social networking sites (e.g. Snapchat, Facebook, Viber or WhatsApp) and the Internet.

> **KEY WORDS**
>
> **Abuse**
>
> Any action that harms or injures another person, either physical, verbally, emotionally or sexually.
>
> **Respect in relationships**
>
> Thinking and behaving in a positive way towards yourself and others, in a way that shows you care about the other person.

Activity

2   Meet Bruno and Elena

 Animation

Read the story of Bruno and Elena and then discuss the questions with another student. Write your answers below.

Bruno and Elena have been going out together for two months. Elena is fifteen and in third year and has lots of friends from primary school and from her local football club. Bruno is seventeen and is in fifth year in the same school. Bruno is quite popular and is in a band. Bruno and Elena got to know one another while they were involved in the school musical. They became friends and then started going out on dates together.

The musical was a great success and over the next few weeks Bruno and Elena spent more time together outside school. They both saw less of their other friends but when they were all together some of their friends noticed changes in Bruno and Elena's relationship. Bruno was often dismissive of Elena and put her down in front of her friends. Sometimes he was aggressive. If Elena was with her other friends Bruno would call her on her phone. He'd demand to know where she was and what she was doing and keep messaging her. He was the one who decided when and where they went, when they were going out together. Elena wasn't happy about this but went along with it to avoid upsetting Bruno and having a row. Elena often missed training or dance classes so she could spend more time with him.

One night, Elena went to her friend Emily's house after she and Bruno had a big fight. They rowed about who should pay for their meal out. Elena felt that Bruno should have paid as she had paid the last time. She told Emily that Bruno had hit her and shoved her around. He'd apologised and said he loved her. Elena said he'd promised it wouldn't happen again, but she told Emily that this was not the first time that he had become angry or aggressive.

A few of Elena's friends were becoming worried and decided to talk to her about her relationship with Bruno and how much they were fighting. At first, she didn't want to hear what her friends had to say but in the end she decided to talk to Bruno. She knew that this might be a bit risky as he might get angry again or even break off their relationship, but she went ahead. Bruno said he was sorry and promised to be more caring in the future.

But over the next few weeks nothing changed. Bruno was even more controlling, and Elena saw less of her friends than before. He kept asking Elena to sext him and often talked to her about what his friends were doing with their girlfriends. He was beginning to put pressure on her to have sex with him as they'd been together now for several months Elena didn't want to do this and they were arguing a lot.

All their friends were wondering what was going on and Emily and Mark, Bruno's best friend, were really worried. They decided to try and help. Emily offered to talk to Elena and Mark said he'd talk to Bruno. They didn't want Bruno or Elena to think they were meddling in their business, but they were getting more and more bothered about both of them, and especially about Elena's safety and the fact that she had become so withdrawn and anxious.

Elena herself was confused and was beginning to have doubts about her relationship with Bruno.

Look back at Activity 1 and identify the ways in which Bruno and Elena's relationship might be a cause for concern.

1. What are you **most** concerned about in Bruno and Elena's relationship?
   _____
   _____

2. Identify four reasons why you think this relationship is not one built on respect and equality.
   _____
   _____
   _____

3. Why, do you think, might this be an abusive relationship?
   _____
   _____
   _____

4 What do you think needs to change in Bruno and Elena's relationship?

_____

_____

5 If you were Bruno or Elena what would you want to happen?

(a) For yourself:

_____

(b) For the other person:

_____

6 What would you say to Elena about Bruno asking her to sext him?

_____

_____

7 What decision, do you think, should Elena make about having sex with Bruno? Why?

_____

_____

Did You Know?

Girls say they are expected to have a 'good reputation' but at the same time are under pressure from boys and their peers to have sex.

Boys say they are under pressure from their peers to appear more macho and ready for sex at all times. (www.b4udecide.ie)

KEY WORDS

Advice

Telling someone what you think they should do in a particular situation.

LEARNING LOG

1 What makes you think that Bruno and Elena's relationship is unequal and worrying?

_____

_____

2 I'd advise Elena to _____

3 I'd advise Bruno to _____

_____

4 What did you learn about relationships from this activity?

_____

_____

Ending a relationship – breaking up is hard to do!

Your teenage years are a time of trying out new experiences and many teenagers have lots of short romantic relationships. Being in a romantic relationship can be an exciting time. You are preoccupied with thoughts of seeing your boyfriend/girlfriend and little else seems to matter. Over time you become closer; you learn to listen to one another, to give and take, to share your feelings and to love one another. As time goes on you get to know one another more and your relationship gets stronger.

Some people may not have relationships until they are in their late teens or early twenties. Other people may decide that a romantic relationship is not for them and they remain single. Everybody is different.

Sometimes teenage relationships last weeks, months or years, and sometimes they don't, and the couple break up. Relationship break ups can be a difficult time for both people. Breaking up can bring hurt, pain and an overwhelming sense of loss which may take you a lot of time to get over, but you can learn a lot from such an experience. When you experience a break up, it seems impossible to believe that you will feel better and that you will get over it. What's important is that both you and your boyfriend/girlfriend are clear about why you or they want to end the relationship.

HOW LUCKY I AM TO HAVE SOMETHING THAT MAKES SAYING GOODBYE SO HARD

– WINNIE THE POOH

PowerPoint

Why might a relationship end?

There are many reasons why a couple might break up. You have explored some in Elena and Bruno's story. Here are some more:

- You grow apart and things that were once important don't have the same meaning any more
- You or your girlfriend/boyfriend may develop new interests and have less time for the relationship
- Feelings can change and maybe you no longer enjoy each other's company
- Maybe you discover new things about your girlfriend/boyfriend that you just don't like
- Possibly you feel the relationship is becoming too serious and you aren't ready for that yet
- Maybe your girlfriend/boyfriend's attitude or behaviour has changed and you don't like the change or feel comfortable with it
- Maybe you aren't sure why but you have a feeling that you are not happy in the relationship.

Activity 3

What do *you* think?

With a partner, come up with three more reasons why a relationship might end and write them below.

1. _____
2. _____
3. _____

Activity 4

Breaking up – what do you do or say?

Zac, Jazzara and Pat are all looking for advice to deal with their relationship dilemmas. They want to know what to do and how to explain how they think or feel, even when they know the other person feels differently. Read through the 'Dos and Don'ts' on page 107 to help you decide what advice to give them. Write it in the space below each dilemma.

Zac's dilemma

I'm fifteen and have been going out with a girl in my school for six months. At first it was great and we had lots of laughs. I couldn't wait to see her at break and after school. Recently things have changed. She has become quiet and can be so negative it does my head in! I've decided I don't want to see her any more and I've sent her a text telling her it's over. She says she loves me and can't imagine life without me. Her brother is on my case telling me she's spending all day in her room and won't talk to anyone. He seems to be blaming me but right now I just want her out of my life and to have a bit of fun again.

WHAT CAN I DO?

_____
_____
_____

Jazzara's dilemma

I've been going out with Luke for seven months. He is good-looking, has a part-time job and all the girls would love to be in my place. When we are out he is great fun and we hang around in a gang. But in the last few weeks things have changed. Luke gets angry if I even just talk to any of the other guys. He resents it when I want to do other things with my friends and he often calls me and messages me saying I might be cheating. I'm not happy and don't want to be tied down like this. I think maybe I should end the relationship and move on but what should I say to Luke about how I feel?

WHAT CAN I DO?

_____

_____

_____

Pat's dilemma

Ger and I are going out for three months now. We are both in TY. I have been so happy. Pat only 'came out' at the beginning of the year but my friends have known I was gay since I told some of them in third year. To our friends we seem very happy together. But lately I've become very unsure and have started to have doubts about our relationship. A friend told me that she saw Pat in town with someone else who looked like more than just a friend. I felt really angry and hurt and when she told me she met up with an ex. I was gutted. This is my first serious relationship and I really felt like I'd met someone I could trust. But I don't think I can trust Pat now and for my own sake I want to end the relationship. I'm not sure how to go about it.

WHAT CAN I DO?

_____

_____

_____

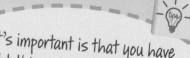

What's important is that you have thought things through and you are clear in your own mind about what you want to happen to end the relationship.

Breaking up respectfully: Dos and Don'ts

Dos

- **Talk** to your boyfriend/girlfriend **in person**
- Be clear in your own mind what **you want** and why
- Decide in advance **what you will say** and the words you will use
- Start by **being positive**, saying what you've enjoyed about the time you've spent together, what you like about your boyfriend/girlfriend
- Be **considerate** of the other person in the language you use
- Think ahead to how the **other person might react** and how you will deal with any possible negative reactions – they might be shocked, hurt, angry and so on
- Be **honest** about how you feel – use **'I'** statements
- **Stay calm**
- **Put yourself in their shoes** and think about how you would feel if the roles were reversed.

Don'ts

- **Don't** allow things to **just drift** in the hope the relationship will fizzle out
- **Don't ignore your boyfriend/girlfriend's point of view** – listen to what they have to say, and talk about how they feel
- **Don't get someone else** to tell your boyfriend/girlfriend
- **Don't** break up by sending a **text message**
- **Don't message** details about your break up on Instagram, Facebook or any other social media
- **Don't be critical** of your boyfriend/girlfriend's character or personality
- **Don't gossip** or bad mouth the other person after the break up.

tips

Many people ask, 'Is it OK to break up by text, e.g. w r thru?'. But think about how you would you if you received a break-up text. It might be easier to message someone, but if you have a face-to-face conversation with them it's more respectful and caring, and shows you're a better person.

Being honest about how I feel in a relationship is important to me because

This can be challenging because

But I think it is the best thing to do because

Being honest is particularly important in ending a relationship so that

LEARNING LOG

Assessment – Check your learning

Staying safe while dating

Not all dates and relationships end 'happily ever after'. Using what you have discovered in the previous activities, work with two others to draw up **'Six tips for safe dating'** aimed at young people. The tips should be specific and easy to understand. You can create a fun poster, make a video or do a PowerPoint presentation – anything that will catch young people's attention and encourage them to look after their safety. You should think about the following:

- ◖ What do you mean by safe dating?
- ◖ How can you keep yourself safe while on a date?
  - • How well do you know the person?
  - • Do you go out alone or with others?
  - • Where do you go and what do you do?
- ◖ How do you tell them what you want or don't want?
- ◖ How do you stay in control and make wise choices? Think ahead – avoid alcohol and other drugs which impair your judgement. Be guided by your own values, especially around sexual activity, and set your personal boundaries (See *Health and Wellbeing: SPHE 2*, pages 145–147)
- ◖ What skills do you need to express yourself clearly?
- ◖ What should you do if you get into difficulty on a date? In your presentation, include telephone numbers of people or agencies that can help, if necessary.

Save your work in your SPHE folder (or have it displayed around your school as a resource for others).

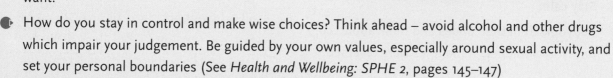
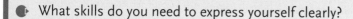

Useful Websites

http://b4udecide.ie – aims to encourage young people to make healthy, responsible decisions about relationships and sexual health. You can hear personal stories from teenagers about their relationship ups and downs

www.kidshealth.org – helpful advice and information on relationships, dating and sexual health

www.barnardos.ie – the Teen help section deals with many aspects of teenage life, including relationships

Review of Unit 2: *The Relationship Spectrum*

1 In this unit I learned about _____

_____

_____

2 I think that this will help me _____

_____

_____

3 I liked _____

_____

_____

4 I did not like _____

_____

_____

5 I would like to learn more about _____

_____

_____

6 This topic links with (another topic in SPHE or another subject) _____

_____

_____

UNIT 3 Sexuality, Gender Identity and Sexual Health

Learning Outcomes:

This unit helps you to:

1. Explain what is meant by sex, sexuality and sexual health ○

2. Become aware of some of the issues faced by teenagers who are transgender ○

3. Appreciate that people in an LGBT (lesbian, gay, bisexual and transgender) relationship can face prejudice, both personally and socially ○

4. Discover what the law in Ireland says about the age of consent for sexual activity ○

5. Recognise the challenges of being a teenage parent ○

6. Learn about Sexually Transmitted Infections (STIs) ○

7. Appreciate that both people in a relationship have rights and responsibilities. ○

(Tick off as you complete them.)

KEY WORDS

Sex
Sexuality
Sexual health
Sexual orientation
Consent
Sexual consent
Legal age for consent
Teenage pregnancy
STIs
Gender identity
Transgender (Trans)

Sex, Sexuality and Sexual Health – What's the Difference?

PowerPoint

In your SPHE classes you have explored many aspects of sex, sexuality and sexual health. So what do these words mean?

KEY WORDS

Sex

As a noun – whether a person is male or female. The World Health Organization (WHO) definition is: 'Sex refers to the biological characteristics that define us as female or male.'

As a verb – 'making love', sexual intercourse

Sexuality

A person's awareness of themselves as a sexual being.

Sexual health

A state of physical, emotional, mental and social wellbeing in relation to sexuality.

Sexuality and you

Your sexuality includes many aspects of who you are:

- Your biological sex
- Your sexual orientation
- Your sexual identity.
- It also includes the processes of reproduction and pregnancy.

Your sexuality is influenced by many factors, including your family, community, culture, media, religion, as well as your attitude to yourself, your values and how you feel and think about yourself. We are all sexual beings, from cradle

Sexual health

Your **sexual health** includes many aspects of health that you have already explored, including your physical, emotional, social and mental wellbeing and a lot more.

A sexually healthy person will:

Be able to end relationships respectfully

Be able to make and maintain healthy sexual relationships

Be comfortable with their body and their sexuality

Understand their body and how it functions

Be able to talk honestly with family, friends and their boyfriend/girlfriend

Recognise and manage risky situations in which they feel vulnerable

Understand the responsibilities, consequences and risks of sexual activity

Know their own values and be able to act in line with them

Be able to access and use health care information and services

Be able to set boundaries when it comes to sex and sexual relationships

Sexual Orientation
In someone else's shoes – being LGBT

From the activities in the previous unit, the Relationship Spectrum, you know that few, if any, relationships are plain sailing. Challenges and difficulties are inevitable, whether you are in a heterosexual or LGBT relationship. These challenges can come from within the relationship or from outside it. For example, while Irish society has become more open on many levels, LGBT people can still face additional challenges in their relationships, their communities and in society in general.

KEY WORDS

Sexual orientation

Who you are romantically attracted to; people of the same or opposite sex.

Let's explore this further by looking at how a person's sexuality and sexual orientation can impact on their personal and social life.

Being LGBT

In *Health and Wellbeing: SPHE 1* and *Health and Wellbeing: SPHE 2* you have already explored some issues relating to sexual orientation and what it means to be LGBT. You should be familiar with the different words, e.g. LGBT (lesbian, gay, bisexual and transgender), and you have looked at some of

the challenges faced by young LGBT people. You have investigated ways in which your school can be a welcoming and safe place for LGBT students However, young LGBT people still face a lot of difficulties. In Activity 1 you will explore some of the everyday challenges faced by young LGBT people and you will try to see what life is like for them.

Activity

1

Walk in my shoes

Imagine that you are a fifteen-year-old in Ireland today. You are living at home with your parents, guardians or caregivers and are in a relationship with someone you've loved for several months now. You may live in a big city, a small town, a village or in the countryside. You expect to do all the things that any fifteen-year-old does.

First imagine that you are heterosexual (straight) and then visualise that you are in an LGBT relationship. Try and see things from each person's perspective and imagine what their life is like as they go about their everyday activities. Your teacher will call out a number of statements. As you hear each one, think about it and write 'Yes' or 'No' in columns A and B below.

Imagine you are fifteen years old and that you have been in a loving relationship for several months	A: You are heterosexual	B: You are LGBT
1 Could you tell your family, parents, brothers and sisters about your relationship?		
2 Could you tell your grandparents about your relationship?		
3 Could you bring your boyfriend/girlfriend to a family party or celebration?		
4 Could you hold hands with your boyfriend/girlfriend as you walk down your road?		
5 Would you be happy to talk about your relationship openly in school?		
6 Can you hope to get married to your boyfriend/girlfriend one day?		
7 Can you legally have sex with your boyfriend/girlfriend?		
8 Would it be easy to get to know other couples like you?		
9 Could you expect not to be hurt or insulted by other people because of your relationship?		
10 When you go out with other friends would you be comfortable giving your boyfriend/girlfriend a kiss or a hug?		
11 Do you see relationships like yours represented in films, online shows, on TV or in magazines?		
12 Could you work in a nursery or a school?		
13 Could you easily talk to your school counsellor if you were worried about some aspect of your relationship?		
Total		

When you have finished, add up the number of 'YES' responses for A and B and write the total. Then answer the questions on the next page and complete the Learning Log on page 116.

1 How did you feel as the statements were being read out?

_____

_____

_____

2 Were some statements easier to answer than others?

_____

_____

_____

3 Why do you think this was?

_____

_____

_____

4 If you are straight (heterosexual) how easy was it to see things through the eyes of someone who is LGBT?

_____

_____

_____

5 If you are LGBT how easy was it to see things through the eyes of someone who is straight?

_____

_____

_____

6 Did you have the most 'YES' responses for column A or B? Write in the number for each.

_____

_____

_____

7 What, do you think, do the results tell you about what life is like for someone who is heterosexual?

_____

_____

_____

8 What, do you think, do the results tell you about what life is like for someone who is LGBT?

_____

_____

_____

9 What did this activity tell you about yourself?

_____

_____

_____

When I was doing this activity I felt

Walking in the other person's shoes was

I think that what other people think might affect someone who is LGBT by

One way in which doing this activity has changed me or the way I think for the better is

Consent and the Law

PowerPoint

You have already explored some aspects of romantic relationships and thought about the importance of being honest in a relationship. Being open about how you feel or what you want is easier in some situations than it is in others. Being able to say exactly what you want or don't want can be difficult at times. It can be especially difficult in situations where you might want to agree to do something, or agree not to do something. **If you agree to do something, you are giving consent.**

KEY WORDS

Consent

That you agree or give permission for something.

You may consent to do things for many reasons – maybe because you want to do something, for example join a team or go to the cinema with a friend. Sometimes you consent to do something because it is for your own good, even though you may not really want to do it, for example staying in to revise for a test when you'd prefer to be out with your friends.

Sometimes you may agree to do something even though you feel it is not the right thing to do because you find it difficult to be assertive and stand up for yourself. For example, if your friend's parents are away and your friend asks you and some other friends to stay over. You know they will be drinking and you are not happy about it, but you don't want to fall out with your friend either.

Sexual consent

Being in a romantic relationship can be exciting and fun but it can also be a confusing time, especially when it comes to dealing with matters of sex and intimacy. These can be difficult topics for a couple to talk about but **it's important that both people in the relationship talk about and agree on these issues**. Giving consent is a particularly important consideration when it involves sex and sexual activity. In Ireland there are laws concerning the legal age for sexual consent.

Did You Know?

In Ireland the legal age for consent to sexual intercourse is seventeen years. **It is illegal for anyone under seventeen to have sex.** Non-consensual sexual activity is also against the law.

It is an offence for a person **in authority** to engage or attempt to engage in a sexual act with a child under the age of eighteen years.

KEY WORDS

Sexual consent

When a person who is over seventeen is free and able to make their own informed decision and willingly agrees to engage in sexual intercourse. If both people agree to have sex, then the sex or sexual activity is said to be consensual.

#AskConsent

To give sexual consent a person must be doing so **freely** and without pressure from another person or while they are influenced by alcohol or other drugs.

A person must also know what they are consenting to. You will only know for sure whether someone is giving their consent if you ask them directly and discuss what you both want or do not want openly and honestly. It is important that you both know when it is appropriate to Stop, Pause or Play!

What does this law mean?

In Ireland you must be seventeen years and over to have sexual intercourse. The law applies equally to males and females and to heterosexual and LGBT sexual relationships.

It also means that, in certain circumstances, someone who has sex under the age of seventeen or who has sex with someone else who is also under the age of seventeen, MAY be prosecuted by the Gardaí.

What are the facts?

Legal age for consent in Ireland is seventeen years.

Could someone be sent to jail if they have sex under the age of seventeen?

A girl under the age of seventeen cannot be prosecuted under the law. A boy, however, can be prosecuted for having sex under the age of seventeen years. The Gardaí and the Director of Public Prosecutions (DPP) use their discretion and look at the overall circumstances of the situation before deciding whether or not to prosecute. (The job of the DPP is to decide whether or not to charge people for committing crimes – in other words to 'prosecute' them). The most important consideration is the welfare of the young person.

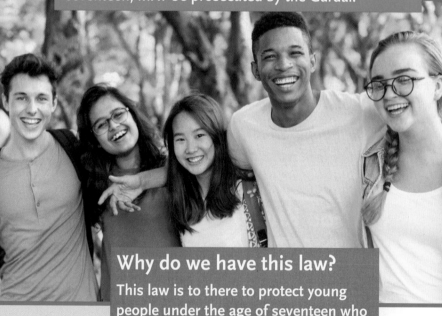

Why do we have this law?

This law is to there to protect young people under the age of seventeen who may be more vulnerable than teenagers of seventeen and over. By law, people under seventeen are not considered to be able to make the decision to consent to sex. This law is also there to protect young people from being taken advantage of by older people.

Activity

2

What's going on? Meet Alex and Pat

 ▶ **Animation**

Now that you know more about the issue of consent and the law in Ireland, read the story of Alex and Pat. In groups of three, discuss the questions at the end and write your answers in the space below. Then complete the Learning Log.

Imagine this situation: Alex is seventeen years of age and in a relationship with Pat, who is eighteen years of age. Alex really loves Pat, and they've been together for six months. Alex has been very happy with how things are going but now Pat would like to move things on and has suggested, more than once, that it's time to think about making love together. Alex has told Pat that they're not ready for this step yet. However, Pat seems to think that Alex is just 'playing hard to get' and says there's no need to worry and is beginning to pressurise Alex to the point that their relationship is strained. In fact, last night Alex had to push Pat away when a straight 'no' wasn't enough. Alex got upset, Pat got angry and now Alex is worried about this and thinks there's a risk that Pat might break off the relationship.

What's going on here?

1 Describe what's happening in this story and say whether or not consent is involved. If so, explain how. _____

_____

_____

2 Why might Alex and Pat think differently? _____

_____

_____

3 Give two reasons why someone might feel uncomfortable with saying 'no' in a situation like this?

_____

_____

4 Alex had to push Pat away. What else might Alex have done or said? _____

_____

_____

5 Whose responsibility is it to talk about consent? _____

_____

6 What risks would Pat take in discussing the situation more openly and talking about what they would both like? _____

_____

7 What risks is Alex taking in not giving consent? _____

_____

_____

8 Do you think Alex and Pat are a heterosexual couple or an LGBT couple? Why do you think this?

_____

_____

Rewrite the ending

Think back over some of the skills you have learned in SPHE which will help you to deal with the issue of consent in a relationship. Think about what is best for both you and the other person involved. Using these skills, write an ending to Alex and Pat's story from the point where Pat is trying to reassure Alex that there's no need to worry. Both Alex and Pat must be happy with the outcome.

Ready to Be a Parent?

Remember

In Ireland it is against the law for someone under the age of seventeen to have sex.

By now you will be familiar with many of the issues to do with your sexuality and sexual health. Taking responsibility for your sexual health means that you understand the responsibilities, consequences and risks of sexual activity and that you can talk openly and honestly with your boyfriend/girlfriend about things that are important to you, including whether or not to be sexually active.

In a relationship both of you have certain rights and responsibilities towards yourself and the other person. Sometimes these rights can be ignored if one person is being pressurised to have sex before they feel it's the right time for them or for their relationship.

Having sex brings both responsibilities and risks. You will already be aware of some risks, e.g. the possibility of contracting a sexually transmitted infection (STI). Another risk is that of becoming pregnant or fathering a child. Having a baby is a big responsibility and brings big changes to a teenager's life. Let's explore this further.

Activity 3

What does your future hold? Your timeline

You are now in third year and may have already achieved some of your dreams or goals. Maybe you got a place on a top school team, found a part-time job or discovered a talent that you have. You are optimistic about your future.

Look at the timeline for the next ten years, starting today and including the years after you leave school. Write some of the dreams and goals you hope to achieve into the boxes, for example, 'Do as well as I can in the Junior Cycle exams', 'Get work experience in animation studio in TY', 'Earn some money from part-time work in fifth year', 'Have a gap year', and so on. Think about your life after school and what you hope to achieve, e.g. travel the world, start a career, be in a relationship, buy your own house, have children and so on.

When you have finished your timeline, talk about it with two of your classmates. What are the similarities and what are the differences? What is unique to your timeline?

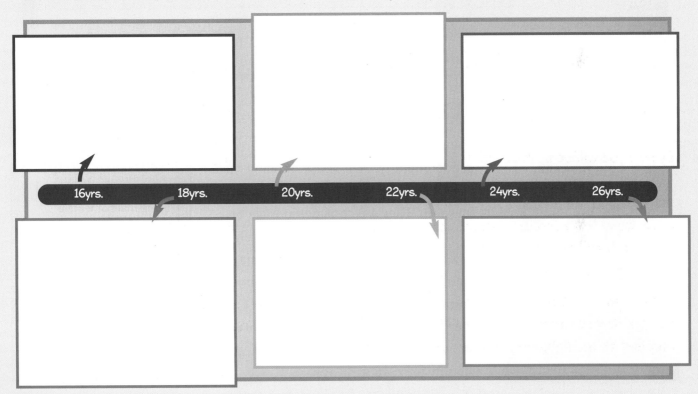

16yrs. 18yrs. 20yrs. 22yrs. 24yrs. 26yrs.

Now that you have thought about your future life, think about how this would change if you became pregnant and had a baby, or if you fathered a baby while still a teenager and in school. Using a different colour, write these changes on your timeline and answer the question below.

Give three ways that becoming a teenage parent, while still in school, would affect the the likelihood of you achieving your goals.

1 _____

2 _____

3 _____

If you are unsure about how to say NO assertively then look at the section on assertive communication in *Health and Wellbeing: SPHE 2* (see pages 95–99).

see pages 95–99

> tips
>
> The only way to be 100 per cent sure of avoiding becoming pregnant is not to have sex. You don't have to give a reason.

I think it is better for me to delay being sexually active until I am older because

Growing Up Transgender

Being transgender means that a person's gender identity, their sense of being male or female, differs from their biological make-up. They are considered male or female but inside they feel completely different. Someone born as a boy may identify with being a girl and someone born as a girl may identify as a boy. From the life stories of some trans people we know that many were aware of their gender identity from an early age.

KEY WORDS

Transgender (Trans)

Someone whose sense of being male or female differs from the sex they were assigned at birth. A trans boy is identified as female at birth but identifies as male, while a trans girl is identified as male at birth but identifies as female.

Trans children and teenagers face huge challenges growing up, including bullying, stigma, prejudice, rejection and isolation. Lack of understanding and support may mean that transgender young people experience a range of mental health issues.

The next activity helps you to understand what it's like to be a transgender teenager in Ireland.

Did You Know?

On 15 July 2015, the Irish Government passed the *Gender Recognition Act*. This allows trans people aged eighteen and over to achieve full legal recognition of their preferred gender and it allows them to get a new birth certificate that reflects the change. Under the new law, sixteen- and seventeen-year-olds will be required to obtain a court order and testimony from a medical practitioner in order to have their preferred gender recognised.

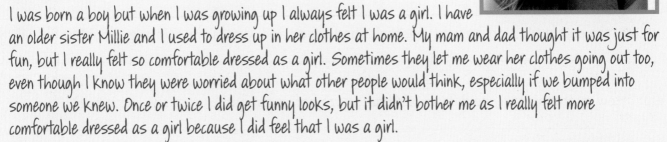

Activity 4

Charlie's story

Read Charlie's experiences below and then, in groups of three, discuss the questions. Write your answers in the space below and complete the Learning Log.

My name is Charlie and I am seventeen years old. Here's my story.

I was born a boy but when I was growing up I always felt I was a girl. I have an older sister Millie and I used to dress up in her clothes at home. My mam and dad thought it was just for fun, but I really felt so comfortable dressed as a girl. Sometimes they let me wear her clothes going out too, even though I know they were worried about what other people would think, especially if we bumped into someone we knew. Once or twice I did get funny looks, but it didn't bother me as I really felt more comfortable dressed as a girl because I did feel that I was a girl.

As time went on my parents began to take me seriously and we were able to talk about it. I was afraid they'd think it was a phase that I'd grow out of. Going from primary to post-primary school was tough as none of my friends knew my secret. It was a mixed school which I thought would make it easier but it was much harder than I expected. I became very sad and anxious, especially in SPHE class when we were talking about puberty and boyfriends and girlfriends. I was totally confused and began to skip school. I kept saying to myself, everyone sees me as a boy but I am a girl!

Eventually the school got on to my parents about my attendance. I was honest and told my mam and dad how I felt, that I am a girl. We told my sister too and she was great. In her SPHE class they had been talking about what it is like to be transgender. I had never heard that word and I was so relieved.

My parents met with the principal of my school and explained what was going on. She was so understanding. I was able to speak to the guidance counsellor who put us in touch with an organisation who helps young trans people. I go to support meetings there now and have made great friends who understand me and accept me.

I'm now in fifth year and have been able to tell some friends in school. Some of them are happy to say 'she' but some of them find it a bit strange. A few were annoyed that I hadn't told them before and a lot of them weren't too bothered either way. It was much easier to be open about it after we talked about the idea of being transgender in SPHE in third year. I know I'll have challenges ahead but for now I'm comfortable being the girl that I am – Charlie.

1 What is Charlie's story about?

_____

_____

2 How do you think Charlie felt when she became aware that she was transgender?

_____

_____

3 Suggest three words that would describe Charlie, particularly in terms of making the decision that she made (e.g. courageous).

_____

4 What difficulties did Charlie have to face?

_____

5 Who and what helped Charlie to face these difficulties?

_____

6 What was the turning point for Charlie?

_____

7 At the end of the story how do you think Charlie feels and what is she thinking about her future?

_____

_____

8 How might this story be different if Charlie were born a girl but felt that she was a boy?

_____

_____

Reading Charlie's story taught me three things:

1 _____

2 _____

3 _____

To be supportive of someone who is transgender I can:

1 _____

2 _____

3 _____

LEARNING LOG

Getting help – where you can get support

If you or a friend are struggling with gender identity issues here are some organisations that can help:

- **Transgender Equality Network Ireland (TENI)** – details of health, parental and peer support. See www.teni.ie or (01) 873 3575
- **IndividualiTy** – a peer support group for transgender people and 14- to 23-year-olds questioning their gender identity, meets at BeLonGTo, 13 Parliament Street, Dublin 2, www.teni.ie
- **BeLonGTo** – does not have a service specifically for under-15s but tries to help by email, phone and one-to-one support. It can also refer parents or young people to regional services. See www.belongto.org or (01) 670 6223
- **The National LGBT Helpline** – Monday to Friday 7 p.m.–9 p.m.; Saturday and Sunday 3 p.m.–6 p.m. See www.lgbt.ie or 1890 929 539

Sexually Transmitted Infections (STIs)

Knowing the facts about Sexually Transmitted Diseases (STIs) is an important part of looking after your sexual health. You should know:

- How they are transmitted
- How to avoid getting an STI
- Where you can get help if you are concerned.

People's bodies are constantly invaded by micro-organisms. Normally you can fight these off. Sometimes, however, micro-organisms reproduce inside the body, causing infections. Infections can spread from one person to another through sneezing, coughing, skin contact or the exchange of bodily fluids, such as blood or semen. Sometimes they can be transmitted non-sexually such as from a mother to her baby during childbirth or through shared needles.

You have already looked at some common infections and diseases in *Health and Wellbeing: SPHE 1* and in *Health and Wellbeing: SPHE 2*. Now you will explore a specific group of infections called STIs (**S**exually **T**ransmitted **I**nfections). You will learn a lot more about this topic in senior cycle RSE.

Remember

This is a sensitive topic. Remember your SPHE 'Class Ground Rules'!

KEY WORDS

Sexually Transmitted Infections (STIs)

Described by the World Health Organization (WHO) as 'infections that are spread primarily through person-to-person sexual contact'. These infections may be caused by bacteria, viruses or other parasites.

What is an STI?

An STI is an infection that is spread from one person to another in one of three different ways:

1. Through close sexual contact, sexual intercourse or the exchange of bodily fluids. Most STIs are spread this way
2. Through blood, e.g. sharing contaminated needles used for injecting drugs, for body piercing or for tattoos
3. From an infected mother to her baby during pregnancy, childbirth or breast-feeding.

Good reasons why you should learn about STIs:

- You will have information that will help you to care for your body
- You will have the facts so that you can make wise choices about your behaviour
- You will have accurate information about STIs, so you will know the difference between fact and myth
- STIs that are untreated can lead to problems such as infertility (not being able to become pregnant), in both men and women, and cancer
- Other skills that you learn in SPHE will help you to keep yourself safe from STIs when you are dating, e.g. decision-making skills, learning how to be more assertive and how to talk honestly and openly with other people.

KEY WORDS

Safe dating

Avoiding putting yourself in any situation where your safety may be at risk when you are dating.

Did You Know?

According to the Health Protection Surveillance Centre of the Health Service Executive (HSE), sexually transmitted infections are on the increase in Ireland. Young people are particularly at risk, especially those in the fifteen- to nineteen-year-old age bracket.

Activity 5

STIs – fact or fiction

What do you already know about STIs? As your teacher reads out each statement below, tick whether you think it is true or false. Then check your answers with the correct ones given by your teacher, write in the correct fact for every 'false' statement and complete the Learning Log.

	Statement	True	False	Fact
1	A person would always know if he/she had an STI.			
2	You can get an STI from toilet seats or in a swimming pool.			
3	Only adults can get STIs.			
4	People who do not have sexual intercourse will not get an STI.			
5	ALL STIs can be cured.			
6	There is a higher chance you will get an STI if you have sex with several partners.			
7	You cannot get an STI the first time you have sex.			
8	Using a condom will help to prevent you getting an STI.			
9	If you know your boyfriend/girlfriend well, you will not get an STI.			
10	You could get an STI through an infected needle when getting a body piercing or a tattoo.			
11	If you have symptoms of an STI and they go away, you are cured.			
12	People who become sexually active at a young age are more likely to get an STI.			

The fact that surprised me most was

because

Some facts about STIs

If you have become infected with an STI, you may not know as you may have no symptoms at all. If you are concerned that you may have an STI you should seek help from your doctor or visit your local health centre. They will be sensitive to your situation and advise you on what's best for you to do to get yourself tested. They will also tell you what to do next if you have actually contracted an STI.

STIs can be caused by bacteria, viruses or parasites. All STIs can be treated but not all can be cured:

- Viral infections cannot be cured, but their symptoms can be treated
- Infections caused by bacteria can be cured with antibiotics
- Parasitic infections can be cured with creams and lotions.

Some signs and symptoms of STIs

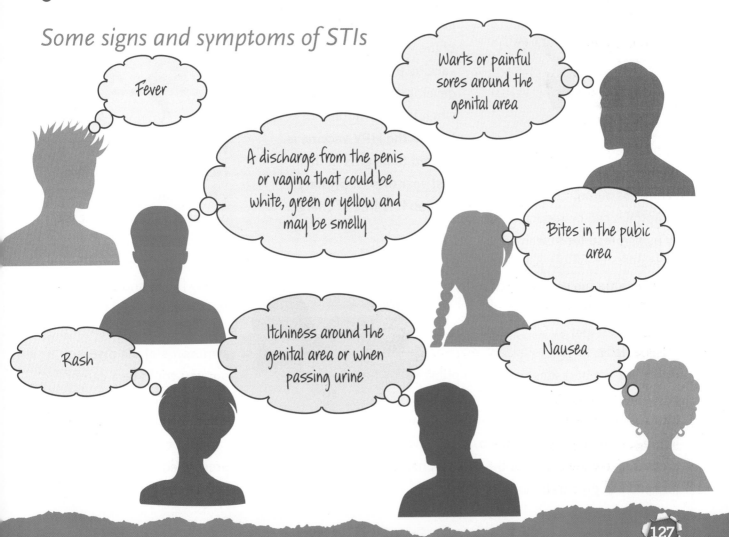

Some common STIs

Chlamydia

Chlamydia is caused by bacteria. It is the most common STI in Ireland. Chlamydia often has no symptoms, so you do not know if you have it. It can cause infertility in women and men and is cured with antibiotics.

Genital herpes

Genital herpes is caused by the herpes virus, so it cannot be cured. The symptoms can be reduced by using prescribed creams and tablets. It causes painful sores around the genitalia in both men and women.

Genital warts, Human Papilloma Virus (HPV)

Genital warts are caused by a virus known as the human papilloma virus (HPV). They cannot be cured. Treatment can reduce the symptoms, but the virus stays dormant (asleep) in the body. The virus can also cause cervical cancer (cancer of the neck of the womb). The HPV vaccine protects girls from developing cervical cancer when they are adults. **In Ireland the HPV vaccine is offered to all girls in their first year of post-primary school. It is free of charge.**

Gonorrhoea

Gonorrhoea is caused by bacteria. It can lead to infertility in men and women. Symptoms may include discharge from the penis or vagina, and itching and burning when passing urine. Gonorrhoea is cured with antibiotics.

Hepatitis B

Hepatitis B is caused by a virus. It can cause liver damage. Hepatitis B passes from one person to another through the mixing of bodily fluids and blood (e.g. needles used to inject drugs). You might have no symptoms of the disease, but you could be a carrier and you could pass it on to someone else. Hepatitis B cannot be cured, but prescribed medication can reduce the symptoms.

Pubic lice

Pubic lice are parasites that live in pubic hair, when personal hygiene is poor. You can see them. They bite and the bites can become infected, causing itching. They can be got rid of by using specific creams. (Pubic lice are not the same as head lice, so head lice preparations will not kill them.)

HIV/AIDS

The virus is called Human Immunodeficiency Virus and the disease it causes is called AIDS (Acquired ImmunoDeficiency Syndrome). It weakens the body's ability to fight infections and diseases. It is transmitted from person to person through direct contact with blood or body fluid with someone who is infected (usually through having unprotected sex, sharing needles that have traces of infected blood or from a mother to a baby at birth).

Symptoms may take up ten years to appear and flu-like symptoms may appear within a few weeks of a person being infected. Once the symptoms appear a person is more susceptible to life-threatening infections. There is no cure for HIV but there are treatments to help people infected with AIDS live healthier and longer lives.

Did You Know?

The Health Protection Surveillance Centre (HSPC) of the HSE records show that in 2016 there were 990 cases of teenagers (15–19 years) diagnosed with either chlamydia (608 cases), gonorrhoea (209 cases) or genital herpes (173 cases). This shows an increase of 8.3 per cent in STIs in teenagers in 2016, when compared with 2015 figures.

Looking after yourself

Having information about STIs is one thing. Knowing how to avoid getting an STI and what to do if you have one is another. Other topics in SPHE will help you here. These include hygiene, healthy relationships, rights, respect and responsibilities in relationships, decision-making, assertiveness and communication skills.

The next activity is an opportunity for you to practise skills that will help you to make healthy choices and avoid contracting an STI.

Did You Know?

The only way to be 100 per cent sure that you will not get an STI is to not have sex and to avoid close sexual contact with another person.

Using a condom, correctly, will reduce the chance of getting an STI but it will not eliminate it.

Activity 6

What's your advice?

Working in pairs, create a role play for one of the scenarios below. Your teacher will tell you which one to work on. In the scenario one person has the problem and the other is offering advice. Read your scenario and decide who will be the person with the dilemma and who will be the person giving advice. Think about who could help, e.g. a parent/guardian, other trusted adult, a friend, GP, health clinic or an STI clinic in a hospital. Plan out what each of you will say and perform your role play for the rest of the class. When all the role plays are finished, complete the Learning Log.

Shelly and Dave

Shelly and Dave have been going out together for three months. They are really relaxed in one another's company and have decided not to have sex until they both feel they are ready. But in the last few weeks Dave has begun to regret this choice and has asked Shelly to reconsider the decision not to have sex. Shelly is unhappy about this, but she really likes Dave. She also knows that her friend, Jackie, picked up a nasty STI from having sex with her boyfriend. Dave says that it will be OK because he will use a condom. What would you advise Shelly to say and do?

How could Jemma help Maggie?

Maggie is fifteen and thinks that she might have an STI, even though she has never had sex. She doesn't want her parents to know, so she asks her older sister, Jemma, for advice. How could Jemma help?

Should Jack be worried?

Jack knows that Maggie has fancied him for ages. At the GAA disco they kissed and now Jack has a cold sore for the first time. He is worried that he may have got it from Maggie and that it might spread and give him genital herpes. Should Jack be worried? What should he do?

Ronan's tattoo

Ronan has saved enough money to get a tattoo. His friend told him where to go and that the tattoo wouldn't cost much. Later, Ronan found out that the guy who did his tattoo was not using new needles for each person. He is worried that he might have caught Hepatitis B. What would you advise Ronan to do?

Write a piece for a blog that gives advice to teenagers who think they might have an STI.

Useful Websites

www.b4udecide.ie – aims to encourage young people to make healthy, responsible decisions about relationships and sexual health. You can listen to stories from teenagers on their relationships and there is advice on sexuality and sexual health

http://kidshealth.org – offers helpful advice and information to teenagers on all aspects of growing up, including STIs

www.yoursexualhealth.ie – an HSE website which offers advice on many sexual health topics, including STIs and clinics where you can get advice and STI testing if you are concerned

www.barnardos.ie – offers advice to young people coping with the ups and downs of teenage years

The Three Rs – Rights, Respect and Responsibility

You have explored relationships from many different perspectives. You have learned that the people in a relationship have certain rights and responsibilities, both to themselves and to the other person. A healthy, respectful relationship acknowledges these rights and responsibilities.

For example, you have the right to be treated as an equal and with respect. You have the right to feel safe and not to be put under pressure and you deserve to be treated the way you would treat others.

Using your learning from the previous activities, and adding ideas from other people in your class, draw up a 'Charter of Relationship Rights and Responsibilities'.

Charter

In a relationship I have a right to…

_____

_____

_____

_____

_____

I have a responsibility to…

_____

_____

_____

_____

_____

_____

Review of Unit 3: *Sexuality, Gender Identity and Sexual Health*

1 In this unit I learned about _____

_____

_____

2 I think that this will help me _____

_____

_____

3 I liked _____

_____

_____

4 I did not like _____

_____

_____

5 I would like to learn more about _____

_____

_____

6 This topic links with (another topic in SPHE or another subject) _____

_____

_____

UNIT 4 Media Influences on Relationships and Sexualit

Learning Outcomes:

This unit helps you to:

1 Understand the nature of media influences on sex and sexuality ◯

2 Be critical of the ways in which different forms of media aim to influence your understanding of sex and sexuality ◯

3 Appreciate that promoting gender stereotyping and sexual objectification of women and men through media and advertising is unhealthy ◯

4 Become aware that gender stereotyping is damaging to both men and women in how they view themselves and each other. ◯

(Tick off as you complete them.)

KEY WORDS

Objectification

Sexual objectification

Media and Your Life

In second year, you explored a range of messages and media influences and learned that they affect different aspects of your life as a teenager growing up.

These included media influences and messages on:

Your gender (being male or female or transgender)

How you should behave

How you should feel

Your sex and sexuality

Gender roles in society, including stereotypes about roles

You already know that media influences can and do influence and shape your behaviour. Otherwise advertising would not be as successful as it is today. Just think about all the advertising you are exposed to every day, either consciously or unconsciously. You see or hear adverts on the radio, TV, billboards, on the Internet and on social media websites, as well as in newspapers and magazines. If you look around you, anywhere you go, there are people are on their phones, messaging friends, sharing photos, watching videos, playing games or on Facebook or some other form of social media. Whether people like it or not the media, including social media, is a part of all our lives now.

KEY WORDS

Objectification

When human beings are seen as objects, not as individuals, but as things to be owned, sold or used.

Sexual objectification

The act of treating a person as an object of sexual desire.

The activities below will help you explore the influences of media messages, including ones which aim to make women and men objects of sex and sexuality. They will help you to understand how 'sex sells' products as you critique three advertising images depicting both women and men as objects without regard for their humanity or dignity as a person with feelings or an identity of their own.

An example of sexual objectification would be an advertisement depicting women scantily dressed or portrayed as being weak or submissive and more sexually attractive. Another example would be where men are depicted with a sculpted 'six-pack' body to help sell a particular product, for example alcohol, aftershave or body-building equipment.

Did You Know?

During adolescence the part of the brain which helps a young person analyse the influences of media is not yet fully developed. This can make young people more vulnerable to media messages, especially when it comes to exploring attitudes, making decisions and dealing with content relating to gender roles, sex, sexuality and sexual activity.

Activity

1

Media – sex and sexuality

From your own everyday life you are aware of the role that media plays. Media messages aim to influence how you think and feel about all sorts of issues, including your sex and sexuality. Discuss the three images below with two others and present your thoughts to the class.

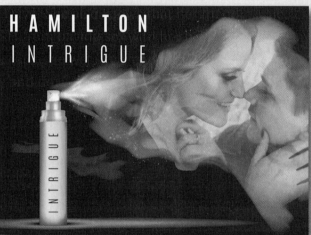

In your group, think about the following questions for each advert:

1. Who is the advertisement aimed at?

2. What did you think when you first looked at it?

3. Why do you think the designer selected that picture?

4. What about the colour and the lighting?

5. What about the faces on the people and their setting?

6. What messages do the pictures give about:
   - Sex?
   - Sexuality?

7. Does the advert convey any other message?

8. How do you feel about the advert?

9. Why do you think a company might use an image like this?

10. How might this image influence the way women and men are viewed by each other?

11. How might images such as these influence young people of your age in how they see themselves and how they are expected to be?

I can look more critically at images in adverts, especially in relation to sex, sexuality and relationships, by being more aware of _____

_____

_____

_____

Sex Sells

'Sex Sells' is a well-known phrase in the advertising industry. It means that over the years advertisements for products related to the fashion, alcohol, car, perfume and other industries have been linked to sex. It is done through the use of sexually provocative images, usually of women, but sometimes of men.

Did You Know?

The phrase 'Sex Sells' is not new. It has been around since the 1870s when an American company, Pearl Tobacco, used this poster to advertise the company's tobacco brand. This type of thing had never been done before so it gained a lot of attention and boosted sales. The phrase 'Sex Sells' has influenced advertising ever since.

Activity

2 Sex and the media

Working in groups of four, look at the ways in which other forms of media can influence sex and sexuality. Brainstorm the ways that sex and sexuality are portrayed in one of the media forms in the table on page 138 – films and TV, video games, magazines, lyrics of songs, billboards, the Internet, e.g. on Facebook, and in other forms of social media networks such as Snapchat, Pinterest, Twitter and Instagram. Your teacher will give your group one form of media to explore.

If you have a mix of boys and girls in your group make sure to get the opinions of both.

Think about the following questions and write your ideas in the table. Appoint a spokesperson who will report back the findings of your group to the rest of the class.

1. What are the messages (e.g. adverts, banners, pop-ups and so on)?
2. Where do you see them?
3. Are the messages realistic? Are they negative or positive? Give examples where you can clearly show how sex and sexuality are portrayed. Are women and men portrayed differently? If so, how?

④ When all the groups have finished, the spokesperson will report on your group's findings to the whole class.

⑤ Complete the table by writing in the findings from the other groups so you have an overview of messages from different sources.

	Sex	Sexuality
Films and TV		
Video games		
Magazines		
Lyrics of songs		
Billboards at e.g. train stations, bus shelters and bridges		
Internet, e.g. Facebook		
Other forms of social media (name them) • • •		

Did You Know?

Britain's advertising regulator announced in October 2017 that new rules are being developed to ban advertisements that promote gender stereotypes, sexually objectify women or promote an unhealthy body image. In Paris advertisers have been banned from showing 'sexist and discriminatory ads' in outdoor public spaces.

Assessment – Check your learning

Write a short blog on why you think advertising which aims to promote gender stereotypes or sexually objectify women or men should be banned in Ireland.

Useful Websites

www.bai.ie – the Broadcasting Authority of Ireland is the regulator of TV and radio in Ireland. If you think a media message is inappropriate you can contact them to make a complaint

www.presscouncil.ie – if you are not happy about a media message in the press you can complain to the Office of the Press Ombudsman and they will deal with your complaint

Review of Unit 4: *Media Influences on Relationships and Sexuality*

1 In this unit I learned about _____

_____

_____

2 I think that this will help me _____

_____

_____

3 I liked _____

_____

_____

4 I did not like _____

_____

_____

5 I would like to learn more about _____

_____

_____

6 This topic links with (another topic in SPHE or another subject) _____

_____

_____

UNIT **1** Positive Mental Health

Learning Outcomes:

This unit helps you to:

1 Identify quick relaxation methods that you can do at school or at home ◯

2 Practise some of these techniques ◯

3 Learn what other students have found useful in helping them relax. ◯

(Tick off as you complete them.)

Practise some relaxation techniques

Now that you are coming up to the end of Junior Cycle and preparing for assessments, practicals and orals, together with making decisions on choices for your Senior Cycle, this can be a pressurised time for third year students. In Strand 4, *Health and Wellbeing: SPHE 1*, you looked at relaxation techniques that you could do to help you to deal with stress. Some of them, such as PMR (progressive muscle relaxation), visualisation and mindfulness take some time to do and involve skills that you can build up over time.

> **KEY WORDS**
>
> Relaxation
> Serotonin

Five-minute stress busters

To help you manage all that's going on in your busy life you are going to learn a number of quick interventions you can use to relax and refocus. Many of these **five-minute relaxation ideas** can be done at your desk, during school breaks or between classes. Taking five minutes to work on preventing or alleviating stress, for example doing a quick stress buster, will save you time in the long run because if you get stressed out you will find it more difficult to concentrate, learn new information and retain it.

> **KEY WORDS**
>
> Relaxation
> The state of being free from tension and anxiety.

Breathing exercise

If you're feeling tired or tense, try breathing slowly and deeply. Put your palm flat on your stomach. Breathe in slowly through your nose and feel your hand rise. Hold for a count of five. Breathe out slowly through your mouth and feel your hand falling.

Keep bringing your concentration back to your breathing and this will get rid of all wandering thoughts!

PMR – Progressive Muscle Relaxation

While PMR takes 25–30 minutes you can do a quick version at any time while sitting at your desk. Simply focus briefly on each area of your body, starting with your toes and working all the way up to your head.

Important

When you're stretching, keep it gentle. Expect to feel tension while you're stretching. If you feel pain, you've gone too far.

Stretching

Sit on your chair with both feet flat on the ground and with your arms hanging by your sides.

Slowly bring your head forward until it hangs as low as possible over, or rests on, the desk.

Starting at the base of your spine, slowly arch your back until it is touching the back of your chair, your shoulders are back and you are looking at the ceiling.

Straighten your head, drop your shoulders and slowly bring them forwards and upwards and then back in a circular movement.

Turn your head slowly, looking over your left shoulder and then your right shoulder.

Take a walk

Can you get five minutes outside to walk briskly during morning or lunch break? If you are studying at home, go out for five minutes – no longer!

Count backwards

Count backwards from any number. See if you can count backwards in units of three from fifty.

Mindful colouring

Mindful colouring is a technique where you focus exclusively on colouring complex designs. It helps to keep your awareness to the present moment in a process that is similar to meditation. You can download designs by searching online for mindful colouring sheets.

Stress ball

Some people find squeezing a stress ball helps them to relax.

Laugh (or smile)

Do, watch or read something that will make you laugh – or meet someone who will.

Laughter not only makes you feel good, but it also makes you more relaxed and has significant physical benefits.

Sit while you eat

Don't stand, don't walk, don't talk – just sit and eat. This helps your body, and mind, to realise that you have taken a break. Food will taste better and you are less likely to overeat.

Drink green tea

It's better to avoid coffee and decaffinated green tea is a good source of L-theanine, which can help to relieve stress. It produces a relaxed effect, without drowsiness.

Sudoku, Solitaire or Scrabble

All of these games are available on your phone. Refresh your mind by playing one of them for five minutes.

Did You Know?

Medical studies in the USA have shown that chronic stress can kill brain cells, and even stop new ones from being made.

Playtime

Play with your pet or younger sibling. A few minutes of rough and tumble combined with laughter is really stress-busting.

KEY WORDS

Serotonin

A chemical found in the human body, responsible for maintaining mood balance. If someone does not have enough of this chemical it can lead to depression.

Have a shower

Negative ions in the air increase the level of the 'feel good' chemical serotonin. A warm shower, with its stream of water and steam, is a quick way of creating negative ions. So having a shower will reduce stress and lift your energy levels. It will also refresh you and wake you up.

Activity 1

Practice makes perfect

Divide the class into groups of four students. Each student in the group tries a different relaxation technique (from the ones that can be done in school) for five minutes. Compare the results in the grid below.

	Relaxation technique 1	Relaxation technique 2	Relaxation technique 3
How easy is it to do this technique? Is it *Very easy, Easy* or *Hard*?			
What are the difficulties?			
How well did it work?			
What might improve it?			

1. When your group has finished, check how the other groups rated the techniques.

2. Are there any relaxation techniques, other than the ones on pages 142–143, that you have found worked for you before?

   _____

   _____

   _____

   _____

3. Which one will you try? _____

LEARNING LOG

For me, the best way of relaxing when time is limited is _____

_____

_____

_____

Assessment – Check your learning

Spread the word!

In small groups, make an A4 sheet giving instructions on 'Five-Minute Stress Busters'. The information should be clear and suitable for laminating and posting in classrooms. Your PE or guidance teachers might be able to help you with this.

Useful websites

www.aware.ie –some good advice on ways to cope with life's ups and downs

www.nhs.uk – in the 'moodzone' there are lots of tips for managing stress, including stress busters

Review of Unit 1: *Positive Mental Health*

1. In this unit I learned about _____

_____

_____

2. I think that this will help me _____

_____

_____

3. I liked _____

_____

_____

4. I did not like _____

_____

_____

5. I would like to learn more about _____

_____

_____

6. This topic links with (another topic in SPHE or another subject) _____

_____

_____

UNIT 2 Mental Health and Mental Ill-Health

Learning Outcomes:

This unit helps you to:

1. Learn about different types of mental ill-health ◯
2. Discover the causes of mental ill-health ◯
3. Understand some of the difficulties of living with mental ill-health ◯
4. Consider what you can do to help people you know with mental health issues ◯
5. Become aware of strategies for minding yourself and others in tough times. ◯

(Tick off as you complete them.)

In this unit in *Health and Wellbeing: SPHE 1* you learned that positive mental health includes:

- Having skills for getting on with people
- Building good self-confidence and self-esteem
- Knowing how to cope with stress and tough times
- Being aware of, and able to express, your feelings
- Being able to ask for, and get, help.

Throughout the different strands and units in *Health and Wellbeing: SPHE 1* and *Health and Wellbeing: SPHE 2* you worked on developing all of the skills necessary for good mental health.

In *Health and Wellbeing: SPHE 2* you examined the link between physical health and mental health, and looked at some of the common mental health issues that young people might experience. This year you will explore what it is like for a young person to live with mental ill-health and what you can do to support them.

KEY WORDS

Mental ill-health

Bipolar disorder

PTSD (Post-traumatic Stress Disorder)

PND (Postnatal depression)

ADHD (Attention Deficit Hyperactivity Disorder)

Clinical depression

Genetic

KEY WORDS

Mental ill-health

A variety of disorders that affect a person's thoughts and feelings, and interfere with their ability to cope with, and get the most out of, life.

Types of mental ill-health can range from issues we all experience, such as grief and stress, which are normally temporary, to more severe, long-term conditions.

In second year you looked at how, in the past, the stigma that used to be associated with mental ill-health stopped people from talking about it and from getting help. In more recent times this is changing. In some ways this is because of famous people speaking out about their mental health issues and about the importance of getting help.

KEY WORDS

Bipolar disorder

A condition characterised by mood swings, from very high (manic) to very low (depression). It used to be called manic depression.

PTSD (Post-traumatic Stress Disorder)

A mental health condition that is caused by very frightening or distressing events, such as war, serious road accidents and violent assaults.

KEY WORDS

Clinical depression

A long-lasting state of depression, sadness, loss or low mood, that significantly interferes with your thoughts, behaviour and physical health.

KEY WORDS

PND (Postnatal depression)

A severe type of depression some new mothers experience, usually in the first four to six weeks after childbirth.

ADHD (Attention Deficit Hyperactivity Disorder)

A disorder marked by someone having problems paying attention, and having excessive activity and difficulty controlling behaviour.

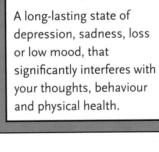

Activity 1

Making links

In this activity there are photographs of eleven well-known people and excerpts from statements they have made about their own mental health.

1 Match the quotations to the celebrities. Write the correct number under each of the letters in the table on page 149.

11 *I was definitely clinically depressed. That was characterised by a numbness, a coldness and an inability to believe you will feel happy again. All the colour drained out of life.*

3 *Not being able to leave the house [because of panic attacks] was so debilitating. I couldn't go to the studio unless I was lying down in the car with a pillow over my face.*

10 *I have lived with ADHD my whole, entire life. . . Growing up I was someone who was constantly bouncing off walls – I could never sit still.*

Alan Quinlan, Irish rugby international

Devon Murray, actor

Gwyneth Paltrow, actor

4 *When my son came into the world in 2006 . . . I was confronted with one of the darkest and most debilitating chapters of my life [postnatal depression].*

Maurice Shanahan, All-Star hurler

1 *The problem with mental illness is people don't look at it as a physical illness. When you think about it, the brain is actually the most complex organ in your body. We need to treat it like a physical illness and take it seriously.*

9 *I felt absolutely alone . . . I don't understand bullying. I cannot understand how you would single someone out and do that.*

Bressie (Niall Breslin), musician, TV personality, mental health activist

Michael Phelps, swimmer and winner of twenty-three Olympic gold medals

2 *I suffer from a mental illness. I suffer from PTSD but the kindness that has been shown to me . . . it's really saved my life.*

8 *I have been battling depression for ten years and only recently spoke about it. It has made a huge difference. If you suspect a friend or family member is suffering in silence, reach out to them.*

Ellie Goulding, singer

Demi Lovato, singer, songwriter, actor

5 *I got really bad. I tried to attempt suicide. I'm glad today that I didn't. You are never alone. Always talk. Even now, I still have bad days, but I know I can talk to someone.*

J K Rowling, author

Davy FitzGerald, hurling All-Star and manager

Lady Gaga, singer

6 *I think everyone is under stress. Health and wellbeing is about how you manage your stress emotionally and how you look after yourself. I've tried to . . . develop some strategies for building resilience.*

7 *For fifteen years of my life, it was never my depression or anxiety disorder that was impossible to cope with, it was hiding it all the time that was the hardest part.*

Answers:

Celebrity	A	B	C	D	E	F	G	H	I	J	K
Quotation											

2. Imagine you are editing a book on mental health issues and how they are seen in Irish society. The purpose of the book is to educate young people about mental health, mental health problems, how we view them and how people with mental health disorders are treated. You must choose one of the eleven quotations from Activity 1 for the back cover of the book. Working in small groups, pick the quotation that, in your opinion, sends an important message to young people.

(a) Which quotation did your group choose? _____

(b) What message does your group think that this quotation sends to young people and why is this important?

_____

_____

_____

_____

Living with Mental Health Issues

Having a mental health issue does not stop you having a busy, productive life. Throughout history there have been people with mental health issues, some severe, who were very successful. Some of them are listed below.

Bipolar	OCD (Obsessive-Compulsive Disorder)	Depression	Bulimia
Winston Churchill	Leonardo DiCaprio	Buzz Aldrin	Uri Geller
Ben Stiller	David Beckham	Pablo Picasso	Princess Diana
Vincent van Gogh	Cameron Diaz	JK Rowling	Elton John
David Walliams	Justin Timberlake	Charles Dickens	Jane Fonda
Lionel Messi		Marilyn Monroe	

Activity
2 Getting the facts

 PowerPoint

The PowerPoint presentation 'Learning about mental health disorders' explains terms, such as bipolar disorder, and other mental health conditions in more detail. Watch it and then answer the questions below and complete the Learning Log. Your teacher will give you a worksheet to complete on the information in the PowerPoint.

1 Select a mental health condition described in the PowerPoint presentation and describe what supports might help someone with this condition in your school.

_____

_____

_____

2 What could **you** do to help if this was someone in your class?

_____

_____

_____

_____

_____

One thing I learned today about mental health challenges that I did not know before this class is

_____

_____

Some positive things I have learned about mental ill-health conditions are

_____

_____

_____

LEARNING LOG

Causes of mental ill-health

Many people live with mental ill-health. Anybody can become mentally unwell. There is no single cause and it can happen for a variety of reasons. Let's explore some of the causes.

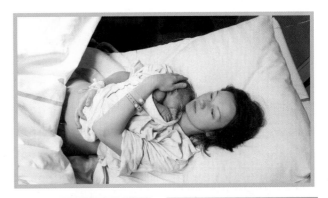

Biological:

An abnormal chemical balance in the brain. A dramatic drop in hormones after childbirth, for example, can contribute towards the development of postnatal depression. Brain injury may also trigger mental health problems.

Psychological:

Trauma suffered as a child, severe abuse, early loss or neglect.

Environmental:

Death of a significant person, divorce, unemployment, failure or imagined failure.

Genetic:

A family history of mental ill-health may make a person susceptible to mental ill-health. However, this does not mean that the person will definitely develop a mental health condition.

KEY WORDS

Genetic

A characteristic of a living thing that is passed on from one generation to another.

Everyone you meet is fighting a battle you know nothing about. Be kind, always.

The importance of opening up

Many of the celebrities featured in Activity 1 were talking about the importance of speaking to someone about their issues. However, we often do not give people a chance to 'open up' or talk about themselves and how they are feeling. This is possibly because you might find it embarrassing or you may not know what to say if they tell you about a problem. Alternatively, it could be because you may feel it's more important to cheer them up or to make light of what's going on for them. But when you do this, you are closing down the conversation. This can make it even harder for people to get help. Let's explore this idea further in the next activity.

Did You Know?

Mental ill-health can affect anybody regardless of age, social class, culture or educational level.

Don't look at therapy or counselling as an admission of failure or as something of weakness, it is the opposite. It is actually an indication of strength. Look at it like if you had a sore knee, you would go to a physio. This is what they do, don't expect to be fixed in fifteen minutes, it takes time. Invest in it, believe in it.

Activity 3

Closing down

Read the four scenarios below, which are examples of somebody closing down an opportunity to talk, instead of opening one up. Then, working in pairs, come up with a way of helping the person to open up about what's going on in their life. Write your 'opener-up' in the space below. For example, you could say, 'I've noticed that you haven't been yourself lately, is anything wrong?' or 'I'm a bit worried about you'.

Lena is one of the top achievers in your class. She works really hard and, as her parents put pressure on her to get the best marks, she gets very upset if she makes any mistakes at all. The mock exams are coming up and Lena is stressed out about the amount of revision she has to do.

Closing down: You say: 'Give us a break, Lena. If you're freaking out, what hope is there for the rest of us?'

Opening up: You say:

_____

_____

_____

_____

_____

_____

_____

Chen's parents always went out to work in the evenings and her grandmother looked after her. Chen was very close to her gran and was really upset when she died two months ago. Since then Chen has been withdrawn, moody and sad. You have tried to jolly her along and suggested hanging out together, but Chen just seems miserable all the time.

Closing down: You say: 'Chen, you can't keep moping like this, you need to pull yourself together.'

Opening up: You say:

_____

_____

_____

_____

_____

Zac is always messing in class. Sometimes it's funny and creates a diversion for a few minutes but now that the Junior Cycle assessments are getting nearer everyone is tired of it. You sit behind him for most subjects and his constant talking and joking is getting under your skin.

Closing down: You say: 'Zac, it's time you copped on and grew up. Everyone's sick of you!'

Opening up: You say:

_____

_____

_____

_____

_____

_____

Ciaran's Dad left when he was a baby and he and his mother live with his grandparents. Since he came to post-primary school Ciaran has begun to think about his father a lot. Sometimes he wishes that he would come back but sometimes he is furious with him for leaving. His grandparents are older now and getting cranky and Ciaran finds them difficult to live with. He is full of aggression, has started drinking in the fields with a crowd you don't like and has dropped out of soccer.

Closing down: You say: 'Look, Ciaran, I know we usually spend a good bit of the Easter holidays up at your house but this year I'll probably stay at home and catch up on revision.'

Opening up: You say:

_____

_____

_____

_____

_____

Mental health is not that complex

There are many myths in Irish society about people with mental health issues. For example, some people believe that everyone with mental ill-health is violent and this is not true. This fear and lack of understanding can make life harder for anyone suffering from mental ill-health. Watch the following animation and do the activity below to learn more about this.

It's OK to not be OK. Some days are just harder than others.

Activity 4

A story in my own words

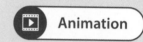 Animation

Read the questions below and then watch the short animation of John's story. After you've seen the clip, write your answers.

1 What stressful event triggered John's illness?

_____

2 What were his symptoms?

_____
_____
_____
_____

3 What did the doctor diagnose John as suffering from?

_____
_____
_____

4 What help did he get?

_____
_____

5 How common is John's condition for teenagers?

_____
_____

6 Who does John suggest could help you if you were worried about your mental health?

_____
_____
_____

Assessment – Check your learning

Helping others, minding ourselves

Using everything that you have learned in this unit, write an advice sheet for young people on how to be a friend to someone with mental health difficulties and on how to mind themselves when they are going through tough times.

When you have heard what other students have written, add their advice to your list if you didn't have it already.

Helping others through tough times	Minding yourself in tough times

Think about someone you know, in your family, your neighbourhood, your school or elsewhere who is going through a tough time right now. Think about what you can do or say that would make a difference to that person. Write down privately what that help will be and when or how you will offer it.

_____

_____

_____

_____

_____

_____

_____

Useful Websites

www.mentalhealthireland.ie – a complete guide to mental health problems, topical issues and treatment options

www.yourmentalhealth.ie – information on common problems and has an online wellbeing workshop and county-by-county supports search

www.mentalhealthsupport.co.uk – advice on mental wellbeing, mental health for young people

www.shine.ie – aims to empower people with mental ill-health and their families, through support, information and education

www.aware.ie – information on depression and bipolar disorder

www.grow.ie – for people who suffer, or have suffered, from a mental health problem

www.pieta.ie – helpful advice for everyone on suicide, suicidal thoughts and self-harming

www.samaritans.ie – information on the listening service they provide for anyone in distress

www.bodywhys.ie – excellent support for people with all types of eating disorders

Review of Unit 2: Mental Health and Mental Ill-Health

1. In this unit I learned about _____

_____

_____

2. I think that this will help me _____

_____

_____

3. I liked _____

_____

_____

4. I did not like _____

_____

_____

5. I would like to learn more about _____

_____

_____

6. This topic links with (another topic in SPHE or another subject) _____

_____

_____

UNIT 3 Dealing with Tough Times

Learning Outcomes:

This unit helps you to:

① Learn about stress and what it means ○

② Understand that the causes of stress are personal to each of us ○

③ Realise that stress has mental, physical, behavioural and emotional consequences ○

④ Examine your own stressors ○

⑤ Appreciate the role stress plays in your life ○

⑥ Gain stress management techniques ○

⑦ Discover how to lessen the possibility of getting stressed by using self-care. ○

(Tick off as you complete them.)

KEY WORDS

Stress

Stressor

Understanding Stress

From all the work that you have done in Health and Wellbeing since you started in first year, you may have noticed that how you feel – your emotional wellbeing – can have a very strong effect on your life and your health. In *Health and Wellbeing: SPHE 1* you looked at ways of building up your mental wellbeing and of minding it through relaxation and mindfulness techniques. Then in second year, using *Health and Wellbeing: SPHE 2,* you learned techniques for building resilience to help you to deal with life's difficulties and challenges.

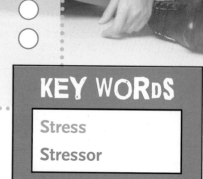

This year, as you prepare for your first external examinations, you will explore what stress is and how it can affect you. You will look at how you can use what you have learned so far, together with some new insights, to manage stress in your life.

Let's start by looking at what you what you find stressful.

Activity 1

Animation

Which camp are you in?

You are going on a camping holiday in Wales with a friend. You must pick either Greg or Gary to go with you. Read the descriptions of each one below and decide which one you would most like to go with for a week's holiday.

Greg has nothing pre-booked. He believes in going with the flow and seeing what happens. He is borrowing a tent from a friend who will drop it over on the morning he leaves. He will throw a few things into his rucksack, which he thinks is somewhere in the attic. He hasn't seen it since his brother used it when he went to Electric Picnic last year.

He has not packed any food; he plans on buying some when he gets there. It's the same with English money. He's just bringing some euro. He doesn't have a lot of money, but he said things will work out. He will find maps when he arrives and you can get the names of hostels from someone. He has his mobile phone but not his charger. Greg loves excitement and he will figure out things when he is in Wales.

Gary has worked out everything. He has checked his tent and sleeping bag and packed his rucksack carefully with essential clothes and equipment. He has changed some money into sterling. He has packed a guidebook and the phone number of his aunt in Cardiff in case anything goes wrong.

He has worked out menus for the week and doesn't want to eat out, as it is expensive. He has booked a hostel for the two of you for the first night and planned a hiking trail that links four hostels, which he has also booked. He has given the details of this plan to his parents in case they need to contact him.

The train leaves at 9.00 a.m. Gary wants to meet at the station at 7.30 a.m. to check everything, to be sure of getting seats and to store the rucksacks safely so you can keep an eye on them.

1. The person with whom I would like to go camping in Wales is _____

2. The reasons for this are

_____

_____

3. What is it about the other boy that would put you off going camping with him?

_____

_____

4 How many students in your class chose Greg?

_____

5 How many students in your class chose Gary?

_____

6 In what way were some of the reasons for their choices different from yours?

_____

_____

_____

The nature of stress

What makes people stressed can vary a lot from person to person. This is because stress is a very individual thing. You will probably find that some of the class would find going camping (or anywhere!) with Greg stressful, while others would be stressed by Gary's level of organisation.

Let's explore this further in the activity below which will help you to see that different people are stressed by different things.

Activity

2 What makes you stressed?

1 In the space write the things, events and situations that make you stressed (stressors).

2 Have a class discussion and, using a different coloured pen, add any new stressors that your classmates came up with to your list.

3 Looking at the complete list, circle anything that stresses other people but does not particularly bother you.

Stress is personal

Stress is connected with how you are feeling mentally and physically. When you are tired, you are more easily stressed. Small things, that you could normally manage, can add up and when they are all combined they can be stressful. You may have heard the expression 'the straw that broke the camel's back'. This means that one small thing, or event, tipped someone past his or her ability to cope.

People react differently to stress and how they manage that stress. For example, you might be stressed because you want to do well in your exams, while another person might think that you can only do your best, and in a few years it won't matter anyway. Some students find speaking in public terrifying, while others love it. It all depends on the individual.

The straw that broke the camel's back.

Activity

3 Different stressors

Find three examples of things, events or situations from your class's list of stressors which stress some students but do not affect others.

1 _____

2 _____

3 _____

The Role of Stress in Your Life

Some stress is necessary in your life and improves your performance. For example, having exams may help you to focus on your studies and to learn more. However, too much stress can cause people to perform badly, because it can affect your concentration, cause tiredness and make you accident-prone. If, for example, you were taking a penalty kick in a cup final, the stress could cause you to miss the shot completely. This happens all the time in penalty shoot-outs. The effects of stress on performance are shown in the graph on the right.

A time when stress affected how I performed was

The effect this stress had on me was

Recognising the effects of stress in your life

People can have many different reactions to a build-up of stress. It can upset your health, your ability to study or your ability to do your job. It can also cause problems in your relationships with family and friends. Look at the activity below and see how many effects of stress you can identify and add to the list.

Activity

4

Stress test

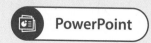
PowerPoint

Mark all the effects of stress that you can think of on his body – two are done for you. Think of the effects of stress on your health as coming under four main categories: **body**, **mind**, **emotions** and **behaviour**.

After you have all shared what you have written, complete your list, adding any new suggestions from other students and from your teacher. Underline the effects that you feel when **you** are under pressure.

Judgement is affected

Tension in shoulders

Some of the effects of stress are also signs of stress. For example, you might realise you are stressed before a big match only when you can't get to sleep, so interrupted sleep is both a sign and an effect of stress.

I have discovered that the way I show stress is

I know that I am stressed when

Identifying factors that reduce stress

Life will always contain some stress or it would be boring. However, if you learn what makes *you* stressed, you can find ways to reduce stress in your life. Some stressors are a part of life, e.g. exams or disagreements at home, so you cannot avoid them. But you can learn to manage this stress so that you escape the health risks that you learned about in Activity 4.

The '4As' of stress reduction – Avoid, Alter, Adapt, Accept

PowerPoint

To manage stress in your life, you can use the **'4As' technique**: Avoid, Alter, Adapt and Accept.

Stress reduction

AVOID

Remove yourself from the stressful situation. Say 'no' when asked to do things that you know will cause you stress. For example, if your friend is constantly talking about class assessments at lunchtime and it stresses you out, try to sit somewhere else or go outside to the yard for a change.

ALTER

Deal with the stress by changing something in your life, or in yourself, that makes you feel stressed out. For example, if you are overwhelmed with study, can you switch a subject to Ordinary Level, join a study group or get a grind?

ADAPT

Change yourself bit by bit until you can deal with what is causing you stress. Tell yourself that it's only for one day and that you can get through it. Use mindfulness techniques and gradually you will learn to cope with what is stressing you.

ACCEPT

Finally, some things that stress us cannot be changed. If this is the case, you must change your attitude and put up with them. For example, if something about your home life is very stressful, and you cannot avoid, alter or adapt to it, then you have to accept it, learn to manage it and avoid letting it stress you.

Stress management

Now that you have been introduced to the '4As' framework for dealing with stress, look at the activity below to see how you can apply it to situations in your own life.

Activity

5   Dealing with your stress

Pick out four examples of stressors that you identified in Activity 2 that could be dealt with by using the '4As' method.

1   A stressor that could be **avoided** is _____

2   A stressor that could be **altered** is _____

3   A stressor that I could **adapt** to deal with is _____

4   A stressor that I would be best to **accept** is _____

Cycle of Stress and Self-care

The more stressed you are, the more likely it is that things will go wrong. You will be more accident-prone, short-tempered and lacking in concentration. The more things that go wrong, the more stress you will have in your life, so it becomes a cycle of stress. As you have seen already, being organised helps enormously to minimise stress in your life. Being rested and feeling relaxed also plays a huge part in reducing stress in your life and helping you to cope with the unavoidable stress that is part of all our lives. Self-care is a really important part of breaking the cycle of stress.

Most of my stress comes from _____

_____

This stress can be reduced/managed by:

1 _____

2 _____

_____

Did You Know?

You can reduce stress by taking care of yourself and organising your life. This will help you to cope with what life throws at you. For example, if you have a big exam the next day you can keep your stress to a minimum and maximise your performance by getting a good night's sleep beforehand, eating a healthy breakfast, arriving on time and having all your pens, ruler, water and so on organised.

Useful Websites

https://ie.reachout.com – easy to read site with information on the physical, emotional and relational effects of stress and with tips for managing stress

www.yourmentalhealth.ie – lots of helpful information on stress, including a section on helping yourself

Assessment – Check your learning

Circle of self-care

The circle shows nine areas where you can take action to reduce the level of stress in your life by building resilience against it. You have already learned about each of these supports through the Health and Wellbeing programme over the last three years. Using a black or blue pen, beside each circle write what you are currently doing in each of these areas. Using a red pen, write what else you could do in each area.

Self-nurture
Yoga, laughter, massage, spirituality, retreats, prayer, sleep, mindfulness

Exercise
Walking, sports, gym

Thinking
Seeing the positive in people and things, avoiding negative people

Relaxation
Reading, watching films, going for a hike

Circle of self-care

Social supports
Good friends, caring family, someone who listens

Problem-solving/planning
Time management, not taking on too much, good decision-making skills

Communication
Being able to say 'no', making 'I' statements, conflict management skills

Nutrition
Eating balanced, nutritious food; minimising sugar, fats, caffeine and food with artificial colours

Environment
Having a calm place to go – home, church, gym, park, an orderly bedroom

Review of Unit 3: *Dealing with Tough Times*

1 In this unit I learned about _____

_____

_____

2 I think that this will help me _____

_____

_____

3 I liked _____

_____

_____

4 I did not like _____

_____

_____

5 I would like to learn more about _____

_____

_____

6 This topic links with (another topic in SPHE or another subject) _____

_____

_____

UNIT 4 Loss and Bereavement

Death and Different Cultures

KEY WORDS

Rituals
Reincarnation

In this section you have already looked at how change and loss are a normal part of life. You have learned about the stages of grief, how grief affects us physically and emotionally and how you can best help someone, including yourself, who is grieving.

This year you are going to look at how death is seen and handled in different cultures and the important part ritual plays in people coming to terms with loss.

Remember

Some of the information in this unit may be sensitive for any student who has lost a loved one. It is important that you remember your SPHE 'Class Ground Rules' and show care and consideration in your comments and contributions.

Activity 1

Images of death

On the gravestone on the right write down quickly all the words that come to mind when you think of **death** or **dying**.

When you have written down as many words as you can think of, mark the words that are 'positive' (+) such as *at rest, rebirth* ; those that are 'negative' (-) such as *grief, loss** and 'neutral' (o) such as *undertaker, grave*. When all the class are finished gather everyone's responses on the board, in three columns – Positive, Negative and Neutral.

> *Note: Grief and the feeling of loss are a natural and normal response to death and are listed here as 'negative' only in the sense that they are unhappy.

1. What is the overall picture of death that is emerging?

   _____

   _____

2. What does this activity show you about people's attitude to death and dying?

   _____

   _____

   _____

3. How healthy, do you think, is this attitude towards death?

   _____

   _____

Rituals around dying and death

There is no correct or universal way to grieve. All over the world people have different rituals that they use to cope with death. Some of these are set by your family, by your religion and by what country you live in. When someone dies in Ireland, for example, they are usually buried after three or four days. However, in the UK it can take two to three weeks before someone is laid to rest.

KEY WORDS

Rituals

Patterns of actions, rites or words that are expected on a particular occasion.

Did You Know?

Elephants will stand over the bodies of their dead companions for several days. When a dolphin dies the males will guard the body until it drifts to deep water.

Activity 2

Dealing with death

Read the rituals below and then answer the questions on page 172.

the questions on page 172.

A funeral pyre on the River Ganges, India

Hindus believe in reincarnation and that when you die your soul moves to another body as it strives towards Nirvana – a state of perfect peace. People try not to touch the dead body as the body is seen as unclean. It is washed, decorated with sandalwood and flowers, and burned to release the spirit. The house is then purified with flowers and incense. One year after the death there is a memorial ceremony called *shradh*, where food is given to the poor in honour of the deceased.

> ### KEY WORDS
>
> **Reincarnation**
>
> The idea that the dead are reborn in another body. Several religions believe that the human spirit is reincarnated and returns to Earth in different forms, again and again, as it strives for perfection.

An open casket at a funeral viewing in the USA

There is concern that American society is growing increasingly uncomfortable with death and dying. While 80 per cent of US citizens state that they would prefer to die at home, only 20 per cent actually do so. The word dead is rarely used. It has been replaced by the sanitised phrases 'passed away' or 'lost'. Caskets are elaborate affairs with frills, flowers and sometimes illumination. Funerals are often by invitation only and the bereaved are generally back at work after three days. Annual memorial ceremonies to commemorate the dead are not common.

Sky burial of Tibet (celestial funeral)

Many Vajrayana Buddhists in Tibet believe that after death the soul moves on, while the body becomes an empty vessel. In much of Tibet the ground is too hard and rocky to dig a grave, and, due to the scarcity of fuel and timber, sky burials, the disposal of a corpse by letting it be devoured by vultures is typically a more practical option. It is what has happened for thousands of years and about 80 per cent of Tibetans still choose a celestial funeral.

After death the body is wrapped in white and placed in a corner of the house for three to five days. The family stops all work, while monks read scripture. The family will choose a lucky day for the body to be carried to the mountaintop, away from dwellings. On the day before the celestial burial, the family removes the clothes of the dead and puts the body in a foetal position. They are not allowed to be present at the burial site. The body carriers (or body breakers) burn 'Su' smoke to attract vultures and lamas chant *sutras* to redeem the sins of the soul. Any remains left by the holy birds must be collected up and burnt because the remains would tie the spirits to this life.

Islam

Funeral traditions differ for different sects of Muslims. Generally, the body is buried within twenty-four hours of death. There is no viewing of the body. It is covered in white cotton and taken to the graveyard by four men. Women are not allowed to go into the graveyard. There is no cremation and the body is laid with the person's face turned to the right, facing Mecca.

For the first seven days of grieving the family is not left alone and friends bring food. The mourning period, when the family wears black, lasts for forty days. The wife of the deceased wears black for a year but the anniversary of the death is not observed. In the Islamic culture, as in other religions, death is accepted and viewed as a natural part of life. The belief that the deceased has moved on to a pleasant afterlife is important and helps the family to cope with their suffering.

Music at a Kenyan funeral

African burial traditions vary widely, depending on the tribe and their religion. In most cases the funeral is seen as a big rite of passage in Africa. The cost can be enormous and is shared by the extended family. In many places burial is on the same day as the death or early next morning so that the spirits will not be awake to block the soul crossing over to a new life.

Some communities dress in white as a sign of the resurrection. Useful objects such as dishes, walking sticks and blankets are buried with the body. Many African communities have a strong belief in the afterlife and the power of the dead to help others. Funerals are often seen as 'going home' ceremonies and music and elaborate parties are common.

Christian

There are many variations of Christianity and their rituals around death also vary. Christians believe that, if you live a good life, when you die your body returns to dust and your soul goes to Heaven, to enjoy eternal happiness with God. There are prayers said at the deathbed and usually the body is laid out in their best clothes in their home or in a funeral parlour, on the day before burial. Friends, family and neighbours call to offer sympathy and to say goodbye. It is usual to wear dark clothes to show respect and refreshments are provided by the family.

On the day of the funeral there is a service held in a church to pray for the soul of the deceased and to offer comfort and support to the family. There is singing and flowers and someone who knew the deceased might give a speech about them. The body is either buried or cremated and a tombstone is usually erected with the deceased's name and dates of birth and death on it.

What parts of these rituals, or **any other rituals you know of**, do you think are helpful for dealing with the following aspects of bereavement:

1 Coming to terms with the death.

_____
_____
_____

2 Saying goodbye to the person who has died.

_____
_____
_____

3 Getting over the loss of the person.

_____
_____
_____

Coming to terms with loss

In *Health and Wellbeing: SPHE 2* you looked at ways of helping yourself, or a friend, to deal with grief and loss. One part of making this easier is to find ways of keeping alive the memory of the person who is gone.

Did You Know?

It is not always the colour black that is used to signify death, as it does in many Western countries: white, purple, grey, green and yellow also mark the end of life.

Let's explore this further in the next activity. Some of the ideas could be done by anyone, while for others you will need an adult to help you achieve them.

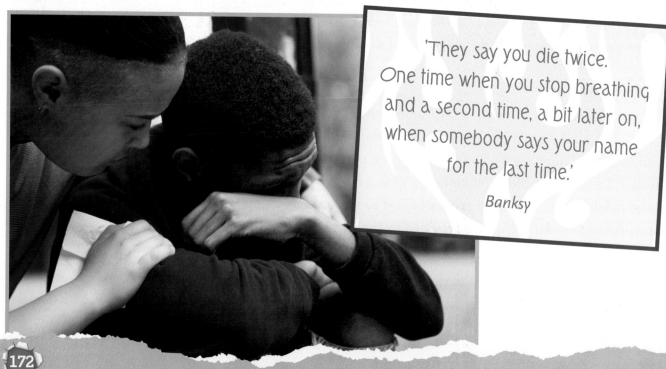

'They say you die twice.
One time when you stop breathing
and a second time, a bit later on,
when somebody says your name
for the last time.'

Banksy

Activity 3

Making memories

Read the list below and discuss with a classmate the ways you would like to remember someone. Write your ideas below and then complete the Learning Log.

Ways of remembering someone

- Plant flowers, or a flowering shrub, that will bloom on their birthday or on the anniversary of their death

- Plant a tree in their memory

- Put a seat in a sunny corner of the garden in their honour

- Mention them and tell stories about their life

- Light a candle at Christmas, their birthday and anniversary. This candle could be placed on the table at dinnertime

- Spray or wear their favourite perfume or aftershave

- Celebrate their 'roundy' birthdays

- Write a letter to them if there is 'stuff' you need to tell them (you can always burn it afterwards)

- Do something in their honour such as running a charity 10K or getting a group to do it with you

- Get a special Christmas decoration in their memory

- Make them proud; be kind, work hard and remember to have fun and laugh.

Add your own ideas to this list:

_____

_____

_____

_____

A song or poem about death which I like is _____

The reason it appeals to me is _____

Assessment – Check your learning

You have completed your three-year Health and Wellbeing SPHE programme. You have learned a great deal about yourself and about how to live in a physically, emotionally, sexually and mentally healthy way. You have developed skills for decision-making, dealing with grief and loss, communication, and building and managing relationships. You have looked at some of the challenges you might experience in life, and learned what help is available and how to access it.

Write a letter from your fourteen–fifteen-year-old self to yourself as a reincarnated newborn, starting out in life and give yourself advice on how to live your life based on what you know now. This letter is private, unless you choose to share it.

Begin the letter: *Dear newborn me, if I was starting my life again I would* _____

_____

_____

_____

_____

_____

_____

Useful Websites

www.hospicefoundation.ie – has a huge amount of information on understanding death and grief and coping with loss, with a special section for young people

Review of Unit 4: Loss and Bereavement

1 In this unit I learned about _____

_____

_____

2 I think that this will help me _____

_____

_____

3 I liked _____

_____

_____

4 I did not like _____

_____

_____

5 I would like to learn more about _____

_____

_____

6 This topic links with (another topic in SPHE or another subject) _____

_____

_____

Guidelines for Positive Mental Health Week

Event Outcomes:

Theme weeks that highlight issues such as mental health, physical health, substance use, bullying, bereavement and so on, help to:

1. Highlight the particular issue ⭘
2. Make it part of the school conversation ⭘
3. Give more detailed information on the particular issue ⭘
4. Make the subject easier for students to talk about afterwards ⭘
5. Ensure students find out where and how to get help if they need it ⭘
6. Validate people who may be affected by these issues ⭘
7. Improve school morale and connectedness. ⭘

Mental health affects many aspects of people's lives, so if you are planning a theme week a Mental Health Awareness Week is a good one to start with. A year group, or even a class group, can work with other groups in the school to organise one. If a week seems too daunting, start with a Mental Health Awareness Day and expand on it the following year.

Getting Started!

Form a committee

Ask anyone who is interested to join a committee and have a meeting to decide on leaders, and on the limit of what you can manage. It's better to organise a few events superbly (and have people crying out for more!) than for your committee to take on too much and make a mess of it. This also discredits theme weeks going into the future.

You should:

- Divide the work out so that people are very clear on what they are expected to do
- Give each person a written description of his or her duties
- Start early so that you allow for things going wrong
- Check the times of state exam practicals, orals, school tours or anything else that might be on the school calendar, so you don't clash with them.

It is vital that the committee members are willing to take orders from the leaders!

Cooperate

Students would find it difficult to organise an event of this spread on their own. For maximum success you will need to cooperate with other groups in your school, including your:

- Principal and deputy principal
- Guidance department
- Students' council
- Parents' council
- Caretaker and canteen staff.

You should also talk to the teachers dealing with: Art, PE, SPHE, RE, Music, English, TY, LCA, Technical Graphics, Materials Technology (Wood) and the library.

Media

If you are going to hold a themed week, you might as well publicise your hard work. This raises the profile of your school and lets people know that yours is a caring and inclusive place to work and study. The most obvious ways to publicise your themed week are on the school's social media accounts, Facebook and Twitter, the school website and newsletter, and on in-house noticeboards and screens.

Members of the school or parents' council may have links with the local paper and radio station, or you could go all out and try for a slot on a TV programme like *Nationwide*.

Planning

Any theme day or week takes a lot of planning and the more time you spend planning, the more successful your event will be. Start well in advance – a month for a theme day and at least two months for a theme week – and keep good records so that you will have them the following year.

Announce your theme week in advance on the school intercom and give updates as events are happening. It is also helpful for parents, or people who were too shy to pick up leaflets at school, if you put background information on Positive Mental Health, and links to other support groups and helplines, on your school website.

The grid below gives you some suggested activities for a Positive Mental Health Week. For this number of activities you would need a large number of well-organised committee members with a small number of leaders. For your first attempt, or for a smaller event, you could pick out a few of the more manageable activities and go with them.

Whether you choose to do a day or a week, it is always good to have at least one event for each year group or to have intergroup events such as a table quiz or comedy club.

Suggested activities for a Positive Mental Health Week

These activities are based on the 'Five a Day for Mental Wellbeing' section from *Health and Wellbeing: SPHE 1* (see page 172). **Your teacher can give you more details on how to organise all the events below:**

Connect	Be active	Keep learning	Give to others	Take notice	General
Table quiz	Mini-sports	Interclass debates	Random acts of kindness	Mindfulness	Lunchtime comedy club
Mexican waves	Zumba dancing	Guest speakers	Messages on lockers	Yoga	Daily joke on intercom
Coffee and biscuits	Healthy meals	Films on mental health	Thought for the day	One-minute stress busters	Short drama
Don't text – talk!	Siege of Ennis	Individual public speaking	Help with homework	Silent walk area	Sculpture competition
Smile wall	Limbo dancing	Literature on mental health	Free hugs	Lunchtime music on intercom	Piece on school newsletter/ website
Drop everything and talk	Keepy-uppy competition	Poster/ photography competition	Plant flowers	Juggling workshop and competition	Inspirational photographs

Remember

Write thank you letters to everyone who helped as soon as possible after the event.

Finally!

Don't forget to review the week:

1 With the organising team
2 With the general school body

Your survey does not need to be a complicated affair. You can set up a quick survey online, e.g. on www.SurveyMonkey.com, and the students can fill it out during an IT class.

Just ask a few questions:

- Year group?
- Class name?
- Male/Female? (If a co-ed school)
- Do you think the recent Positive Mental Health Week was worthwhile? Yes/No
- What did you like?
- What did you not like?
- What would you like more of?

NOTES

NOTES

NOTES